BIOFEEDBACK AND SOMATICS

TOWARD PERSONAL EVOLUTION

Dedicated to Eleanor David,
Thomas Hanna, and Clyde

BIOFEEDBACK AND SOMATICS

TOWARD PERSONAL EVOLUTION

ELEANOR CRISWELL-HANNA

Freeperson Press
Novato, California

Cover Design: Dunham Bergquist + Associates
Cover Image: Stephen E. Wall
Interior Design and Typesetting: TBH/Typecast, Inc.
Printing and Binding: McNaughton & Gunn

Printed in the United States of America
ISBN: 0-918236-06-1
First Edition: 1995

Published by Freeperson Press
455 Ridge Road
Novato, California 94947

ACKNOWLEDGMENTS

Figures on pages 18, 20, 72, 91, 92, 184, 185, 187, 189, and 191 from *Survey of Functional Neuroanatomy* (third edition) by Bill Garoutte, Ph.D., M.D. Copyright © 1994 by Mill Valley Medical Publishers. Reprinted with permission of the author and publisher.

Figures on pages 106 and 114 by Bill Garoutte, Ph.D., M.D.

Figures on page 90 from *The Body of Life* by Thomas Hanna. Copyright © 1993 by Thomas Hanna. Publisher, Healing Arts Press. Reprinted by permission of Eleanor Criswell-Hanna.

Figures on pages 32, 33, and 34 from *Somatics* by Thomas Hanna. Copyright © 1988 by Thomas Hanna. Publisher, Addison-Wesley. Reprinted by permission of Eleanor Criswell-Hanna.

Figures on pages 8, 9, 10, 63, 76, 77, 78, 84, 88, 103, and 116 are graphs from the Biofeedback Training and Research Institute, Cotati, California. Reprinted by permission of Stephen E. Wall, Director.

Photos on pages 4, 38–39, 60, and 161 are by Media Services, Sonoma State University; p. 30 by Joel Gordon. Reprinted by permission of Joel Gordon.

Figures on pages 133 and 136 are by Pamela Robertson, from *How Yoga Works* by Eleanor Criswell. Copyright © by Eleanor Criswell. Published by Freeeperson Press. Reprinted by permission of Eleanor Criswell-Hanna.

Cover image by Stephen E. Wall, mandala computerized biofeedback display; back cover photo by Clyde.

CONTENTS

PART II
Biofeedback, Relaxation and Performance

ILLUSTRATIONS

PREFACE

Many years ago, because of my interest in the development of human potential, I became excited by the possible contribution of biofeedback to the cultural evolution of humans. Many of us had a similar vision. Freedom and autonomy in the actualization of positive human potential is crucial. The possibilities for the use of psychophysiological measures in evaluation of the impact of developmental experiences are tremendously exciting. Biofeedback has made it possible to go one step further: to use our own physiological measures as feedback to us about the effects of life experiences, and therefore, to make changes in our physiology and behavior. Somatics, in general, is a nontechnological approach to self-regulation. This is freedom and autonomy (self-regulation) manifested at a physiological level.

We cannot depend solely on others to care for our health, well being, and maximum development of our potential. This is more and more the case. But we can become highly skilled at being our own somatic educators, and we can share that knowledge with those with whom we live and work. With these biofeedback and somatic skills, we can actualize a great deal of our potential for health and well being throughout our lives.

The purpose of this book is to provide a comprehensive foundation for understanding the field of biofeedback and somatics. Whether you are just beginning in the field, want to augment your basic understanding of it, or are an educated layperson wanting to know what it is, this book is designed to enable you to learn the important concepts of biofeedback and somatics. You can make them a part of your life. They can be used by people who are training to become biofeedback practitioners, or by people who are using biofeedback and somatics for their own self-care and development.

WHAT IS BIOFEEDBACK?

Biofeedback is simply the feeding back of a biological signal to you, the producer of the signal. The biological signals are recorded by electronic devices. Through the information provided, you become able to change your physiological state in a desired direction. The information fed back is significant with regard to a predetermined goal.

The field of biofeedback has gone through a period of professionalization. Standardization, consistency, and continuity with the other health care delivery systems have been of great concern. Yet the biofeedback practitioner must work creatively to achieve goals in a way that is workable for the client.

Some practitioners work as biotherapists with biofeedback at the core of their practice. How biofeedback is used by the different disciplines depends on the structure of the practice or the discipline. The psychologist tends to use the one-on-one, 50-minute hour approach to biofeedback. The physician or practitioner in a medical setting often uses a 30-minute session. The physical therapist may also use a 30-minute session in conjunction with other physical therapy interventions. The structure selected is appropriate for the patient/client population and treatment plans found in that setting.

There are two basic theories as to how biofeedback works; there are other speculations of interest. The two basic theories are behaviorism and information theory. The behavioristic theory of biofeedback rests on the idea that the feedback signal is a reinforcer. The information theory of biofeedback refers to the idea that biofeedback provides the person with information about his or her body's function. With increased information there is a more effective use of the body on many levels.

Biofeedback training can affect a person's locus of control, usually shifting it from external to internal. This means that people with an external locus of control, who usually feel that their lives are controlled by others and by circumstances, come to develop a more internal locus of control, feeling that they can impact on their environments and make decisions about how to react and make changes. Biofeedback offers a person some choice and flexibility with regard to which stance is chosen as a way of experiencing the world.

People often ask me how I became involved in biofeedback. Originally, I became involved because of my interest in electroencephalography (the recording of brain waves). I remember the moment I first read about electroencephalography (referred to as EEG). I was whiling away some time in the library of a naval installation in Norfolk, Virginia. I happened to browse through a book by Grey Walter, the British brain researcher, titled *The Living Brain.* Suddenly, in a burst of insight, I realized that the way to measure the impact of learning on brain changes might be through measuring the EEG before and after learning.

I was intensely excited.

From there I continued my literature review of EEG. I moved to Gainesville, Florida, to continue my doctoral work at the University of Florida. I volunteered to do some work in the EEG lab at the Veterans Administration hospital in Gainesville. There I was able to learn some of the principles of electroencephalography, under the gracious tutelage of Frances Matthews, EEG technician.

During the summer of 1967, I lived in Laguna Beach, California. In exploring the area for EEG research, I happened upon the work of Joseph Hart, Ph.D., a professor at the University of California at Irvine. He was engaged in doing some of the first biofeedback studies. His research dealt with the relationship between hypnotic susceptibility and the capacity to increase the presence of alpha waves through biofeedback. (They found that there was a significant correlation between susceptibility to hypnosis and ability to succeed in alpha training.)

Joseph Hart kindly invited me to participate in the activities. I engaged in a literature review of relevant materials, and we met periodically to discuss the findings. I rode my motorcycle up the coast highway in order to spend time in the campus library and in his biofeedback lab. It was an invaluable experience, and a wonderful way of pursuing my interest in biofeedback.

When I returned to Gainesville from the summer break, I continued my EEG studies. Joe Hart formed an information exchange network of 17 researchers who would exchange letters and papers about biofeedback. I was excited to have been included in that group; I was very excited about the potential of biofeedback.

When I moved to the San Francisco Bay Area, I met Joe Kamiya. I began to study with him on a formal and informal basis (he held small electronics and EEG biofeedback classes, and he was very generous with his knowledge and his time). A group of early biofeedback visionaries would meet to discuss the potential of biofeedback. Results of those discussions and writings were published in an article in one of Bob Ornstein's books attributed to Ralph Ezios. (Ralph was a favorite name of Bob Ornstein, and Ezios stood for Electric Zen in Outer Space. Barbara Brown had decided that she preferred to be mentioned in a footnote rather than as an author. So we all dropped to the footnote and left authorship to the fictional "Ralph.")

I was hired at Sonoma State University to teach physiological psychology in the Fall of 1969, and a Beckman EEG was bought for the Psychology Department so that I could use it in my classes. Special circuitry enabled us to use it as an EEG biofeedback device. We began to use it in the physiological psychology class. Later, the biofeedback and consciousness research class was created because of student demand. As they say, the rest is history. It has been a great privilege to participate in the history of biofeedback. Biofeedback research and application is now worldwide. It has gone a long way toward fulfilling the early potential we all envisioned.

BIOFEEDBACK AND SOMATICS

"Somatics" is a term coined by Thomas Hanna in 1976. He used the term to label the field that was beginning to develop which included the mind/body integration disciplines.

He used the term "soma," the Greek word for the living body, to label this mind-body combination. He then defined it as the body experienced from within. It is his brilliant solution for the mind-body problem.

Biofeedback is primarily a matter of somatic practice. It includes the first- and third-person perceptions. First-person perception refers to your personal perceptions about yourself from your subjective center. You are "subject" and everything else is considered an "object." The third-person perception is the outside information about the person. It includes information about how a person behaves, the observations of the biofeedback practitioner, and external observations of the biofeedback instrument.

As Thomas Hanna would say, the biofeedback is being done by the body of life. The biofeedback instrument is recording information about the life processes: the physiological functions and whether they are on or off homeostasis (which is the balance point). With the aid of biofeedback information, one is able to guide oneself in directions appropriate for the task. That means that one is sometimes moving toward homeostasis and sometimes away.

With biofeedback training one is trying to make conscious functions that are usually unconscious; trying to make voluntary that which is usually involuntary. That means that functions that are usually automatically controlled by the brain stem will be controlled at the cortex level where one can organize oneself more effectively to meet one's needs.

We are not used to consciously controlling the autonomic systems, as we are used to controlling other systems (for example, the muscular system). We do consciously control the central nervous system (CNS) to some extent, but we are not aware of ourselves as we do it. We do control the CNS indirectly, for example, through behavioral control, but we do not usually exert cognitive and affective control (although certain branches of therapy approach conscious cognitive and affective control).

With biofeedback, we use the equipment to amplify the signals we generate. With the evidence of autonomic function brought up to a level that can be perceived, we are able to work toward conscious control.

Therefore, we take time to practice controlling the function. There are certain strategies that intensify the function so that we may control it. All of this involves the conscious mind in controlling the function. Therefore, various areas of the voluntary motor cortex and other areas of the cerebral cortex are more involved in controlling the function. Awareness is a key factor.

As a result of training, when you return to everyday activities, you organize all of your psychophysiological systems more effectively for the tasks at hand.

This book will enable you to develop a basic understanding of biofeedback and somatics. We will explore biofeedback and somatics; an introduction to biofeedback training; the concepts of stimulation, arousal, and adaptation level; indications for biofeedback; contraindications for biofeedback; training and instrumentation; electroencephalograph feedback; electromyograph feedback; electrodermal feedback; skin temperature feedback; adjunctive procedures; biofeedback, relaxation and performance; biofeedback and stress management; biofeedback in education; biofeedback in the business setting; and biofeedback and optimal performance, athletics, and the arts. The appendices include an overview of biofeedback and the nervous systems; a biofeedback protocol for lab or home practice; a stress management protocol; and biofeedback and somatics resources. The main purpose of the book is to provide a framework for your continued learning and experience.

••••••••••••

There have been many people involved in the development of my understanding of biofeedback and somatics. I would like to thank: Francis Matthews, Gainesville, Florida, EEG Lab, V.A. Hospital, for her fostering of my original EEG apprenticeship; Joe Hart, for his encouragement of my exploration of EEG biofeedback; Joe Kamiya, for his tutelage in EEG biofeedback and electronics; the many friendships within the Association for Applied Psychophysiology and Biofeedback (especially, Francine Butler), and the Biofeedback Society of California; Elmer and Alyce Green and the Council Groves Conference (Kansas); and my colleagues Victor Daniels, Arthur Warmoth, David Van Nuys, and Barry Godolphin, great friends of the Biofeedback Labs at Sonoma State University.

I want to thank the students within the Sonoma State University Biofeedback Professional Training sequence, who have gone on to become wonderful professionals in the field, and the students in the classes who were primarily interested for their own somatic awareness and development and went on to use the information personally and professionally in other ways. Special thanks to Kathleen Branson, Heide Harris, Patrick McKee, Lynda Moore, Katy Throop, Bruce Geesey, and, especially, Lorna Cunkle, who contributed to the index.

Thanks to my family, Norman Marshall Camp, M.D., Sydney Fleischer, Marshall Camp, Lee Camp and Dean Camp, for their continued encouragement.

Within the field of somatics, my deep gratitude is to Moshe Feldenkrais (a continuing inspiration to me), Yochanan Rywerant and Yardena Alotin (who encouraged me to complete this book), and Thomas Hanna, who made the wonderful connection between somatics and biofeedback, through our many years of dialogue.

A special thanks to Stephen Wall for our years of conversations and collaboration, his close reading of the manuscript, and the use of his wonderful graphs throughout the book and the cover; Bill Garoutte for his encouragement, years of sharing of his functional neuroanatomical and electroencepholographic information, and the use of his neuranatomical illustrations; and Katee Wynia for her careful reading of the manuscript.

I want to thank Marsha Calhoun for her extensive editorial assistance and guidance; Allegra Hiner and Sam Hiner for their work with Somatics Educational Resources and as support staff for the development of this book; Jane Bowerman and Rosemary Hopp for their staff support; Dunham-Bergquist + Associates for the cover design; TBH/Typecast for its typesetting, book design, assistance with illustrations and general encouragement; and McNaughton and Gunn for their excellent book production.

PART I

Introduction to Biofeedback and Somatics

CHAPTER ONE

INTRODUCTION TO BIOFEEDBACK TRAINING

"Biofeedback may be defined as the technique of using equipment (usually electronic) to reveal to human beings some of their internal physiological events, normal and abnormal, in the form of visual and auditory signals in order to teach them to manipulate these otherwise involuntary or unfelt events by manipulating the displayed signals."

JOHN V. BASMAJIAN

"Going through biofeedback training was such an empowering experience. Because I am so much more aware of my responses and what they mean for me, my everyday stresses don't have as much impact on my life. Being aware of the processes my body goes through enables me to make whatever adjustments are needed."

MARION SVIHULA, BIOFEEDBACKER

SELF-REGULATION

The name of the game in biofeedback is self-regulation (Figure 1.1). Self-regulation refers to the function of assessing yourself and the situation, deciding on your direction, and making changes in your physiology or behavior to correct the situation. The biofeedback experience varies, as does the degree to which self-regulation is emphasized. For example, you may decide to warm your hands for a particular purpose, such as a health issue, or just because they are cold. Or you may decide to change elements in your lifestyle toward ones that are more health promoting.

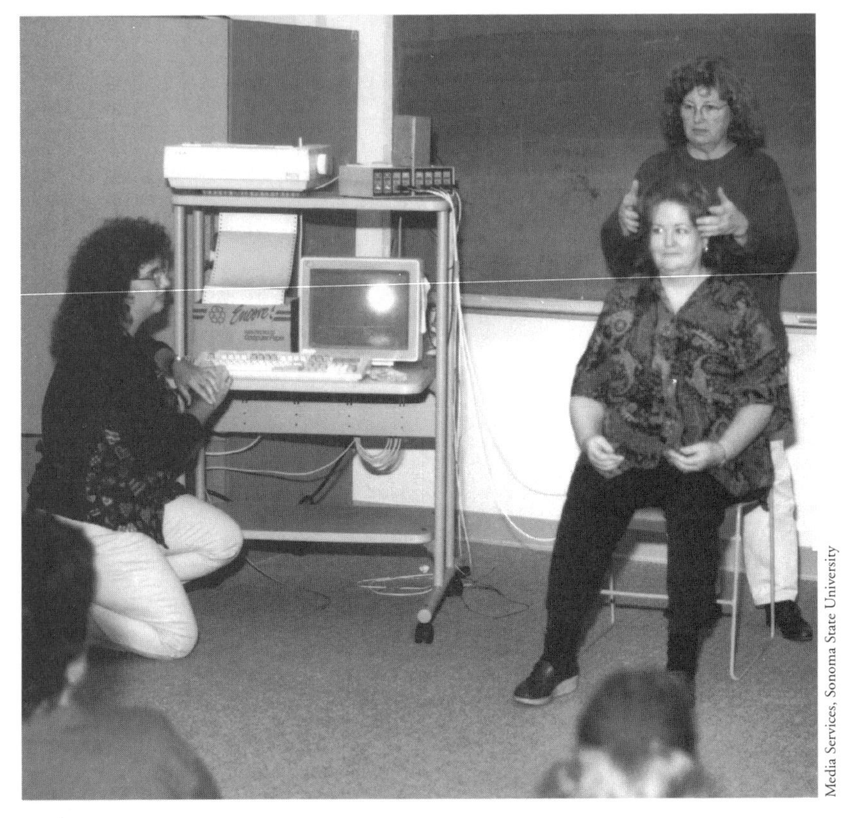

Media Services, Sonoma State University

FIGURE 1.1
Biofeedback system, Psychology Department, Sonoma State University. Students demonstrating biofeedback-assisted self-regulation in the classroom. (Elizabeth Boles, Donna Jenkins, Lynda Moore, and others.)

The concept of self-regulation has implications for every aspect of your life. You are moving through your world with varying degrees of self-direction or proaction with regard to dealing with it. Often you are in a reactive mode: something happens and you respond.

It has been said that the adult learner learns something for a purpose. Therefore, to maximize the learning experience it is valuable to define a purpose that is motivating. This might concern better health, job performance, or greater responsiveness in your relationships.

NATURAL SELF-REGULATION

Biofeedback (self-regulation) is a natural part of the body's functions. The primary goal of ongoing self-regulation is homeostasis, the balance an organism must achieve to sustain life. Moment by moment, you assess various levels of activity in various body systems, such as temperature, fluid content of cells, electrolyte balance, etc. Then physiological functions come into play to return the body to the desired levels if it is off homeostasis.

SUBCONSCIOUS PHYSIOLOGICAL FUNCTIONS

Biofeedback measures subconscious physiological functions. These functions are then processed and amplified, until they are brought up to the level where the trainee can perceive them.

PSYCHOPHYSIOLOGICAL TRAINING

Psychophysiological training includes measuring psychophysiological events, feeding this back to you, and allowing you to practice increasing or decreasing levels of activity. As training goes on, training may also include practice in creating patterns of psychophysiological response for particular purposes, as well as practice geared generally toward increased physiological cohesiveness and decreased fractionation, which leads to greater integration and organization at other times. Developmental, multimodality biofeedback training in the lab helps you create skills that are used in a variety of settings.

With research on optimal psychophysiological levels and patterns for particular tasks, such as the work of Maurice B. Sterman, it may soon be possible to train to match psychophysiological criteria for skilled performance.

GENERALIZATION OF TRAINING

Once you have worked with the biofeedback equipment, you will be able to take this learning into situations without the equipment, to generalize the training. This happens with some people who readily and cleverly notice situations in which they can utilize their skills. Other people need more specific guidance in seeing how to take what they have learned into their daily lives.

BENEFITS OF BIOFEEDBACK

After biofeedback training, you will be more effective in what you do, more able to attend to the event at hand, more able to concentrate and clear your thoughts, and more able to remember experiences. Your memories will have greater clarity.

In addition, you have more of a feeling of being able to deal with situations. The capacity to self-regulate means that you can confront situations with a view to problem-solving, finding some viable solution.

BIOFEEDBACK AS A DISCOVERY PROCESS

Sometimes a person engaged in biofeedback training can discover things he or she never knew were possible because of the change of focus involved in the training. It brings in many ways of looking at yourself and your life, simply because you have never looked at yourself from that vantage point.

MIRACLES

Sometimes "miracles" occur in biofeedback. When the therapist and client are supported by instrumentation and displays of the client's physiological activity, a spark may be ignited within the client which may mobilize hope, motivation, self-esteem, and self-efficacy. It is quite an empowering process. Even with a more recalcitrant client, it is sometimes possible to get a message through that transforms what is possible in the session.

Miracles in biofeedback come when all the ingredients for a full response to the experience are in place. When we line up all the elements—appropriate trainer and client match, readiness for change on the part of the client, environmental support, responsive physiology, etc.—there is sometimes an extra ingredient which is like a blessed alchemical process. It is like a state of grace, a special reality that the trainer and the client enter together, in which they are able to do things that transcend the ordinary. This is an inspired, exhilarating state.

DEVELOPMENTAL ASPECTS

Biofeedback may be used as a means of continuing general personal development, rather than for the specific purpose of symptom removal (Figures 1.2, 1.3, and 1.4). This does not involve just skills training or preparation for skilled performance, but rather provides you with a sense of moving forward developmentally, toward continued actualization of psychophysiological potential. The person who goes through this training will function at a different developmental level than others who have not had such training.

BIOFEEDBACK AS A DEVELOPMENTAL EXPERIENCE

Biofeedback is most often an intervention that is used when the person develops a problem. However, biofeedback training should be part of the developmental experience. Children should be trained from infancy on in the art and science of self-regulation. What would be the result of being raised in this manner? In the first place, such persons would have a sense of confidence and self-efficacy that is currently unheard of. They would enter situations evaluating the factors and the best way of organizing themselves and the environment for maximum effectiveness. They would have a trained tendency to form goals, evaluate effectiveness, and alter their course of action in a very practical and realistic manner. They would also have a tendency to maintain health on an ongoing basis, and to honor the environment as it supports health.

EARLY DEVELOPMENTAL EXPERIENCES

Biofeedback needs to be a part of the early developmental experience. The skills of self-regulation need to be taught throughout life, also. This means that childhood experiences in assessment, planning, implementation of the plan, and evaluation need to be conducted by caregiver and child. In addition, the parent needs to model this for the child in everyday life.

JUGGLING

Becoming a biofeedback practitioner is an experience of learning a special juggling act. This learning becomes something that generalizes to other parts of your life.

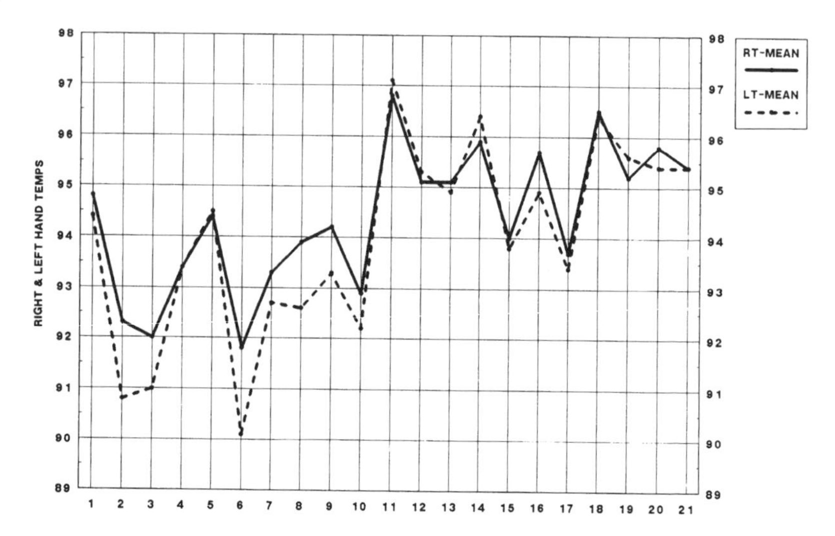

FIGURE 1.2A
Right and left temperature means across 21 sessions (Client A.A.) Thermistor placements were on the volar surface of the ring finger of the right and left hand.

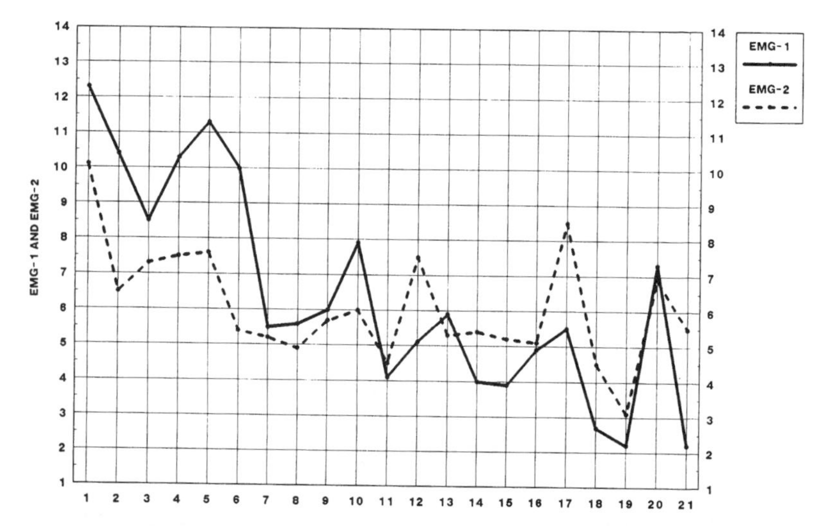

FIGURE 1.2B
EMG microvolt measures across 21 sessions (Client A.A.) EMG-1 electrode placement is on the right and left anterior temporalis muscles; EMG-2 electrode placement is on the right and left upper trapezius muscles (across the shoulders).

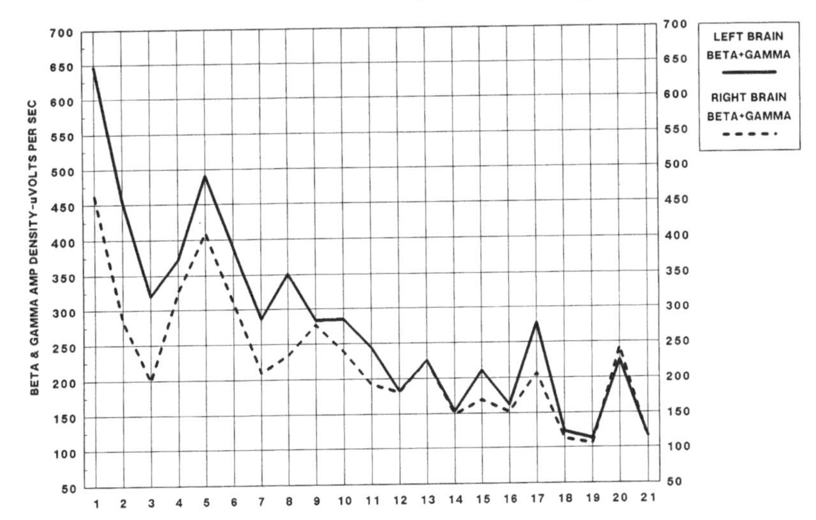

FIGURE 1.3A
Left and right hemisphere beta and gamma brain wave frequencies (13–35 Hz) (session means) across 21 sessions (Client A.A.) Common reference sensor is placed in the center of the forehead; occipital lobe (global hookup) placements on 01 and 02.

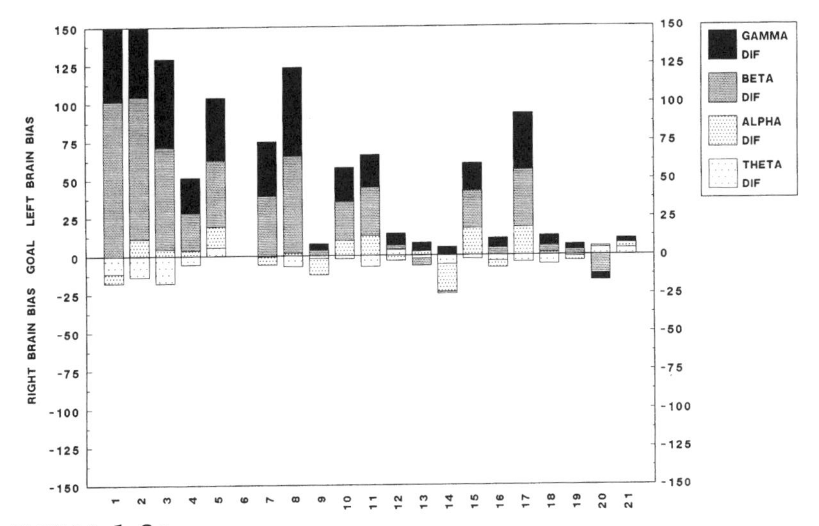

FIGURE 1.3B
Right hemisphere versus left hemisphere brain wave differences across 21 sessions (Client A.A.) Zero equals balance. Amplitude density represents microvolts per second. Notice the trend toward balance between the two hemispheres.

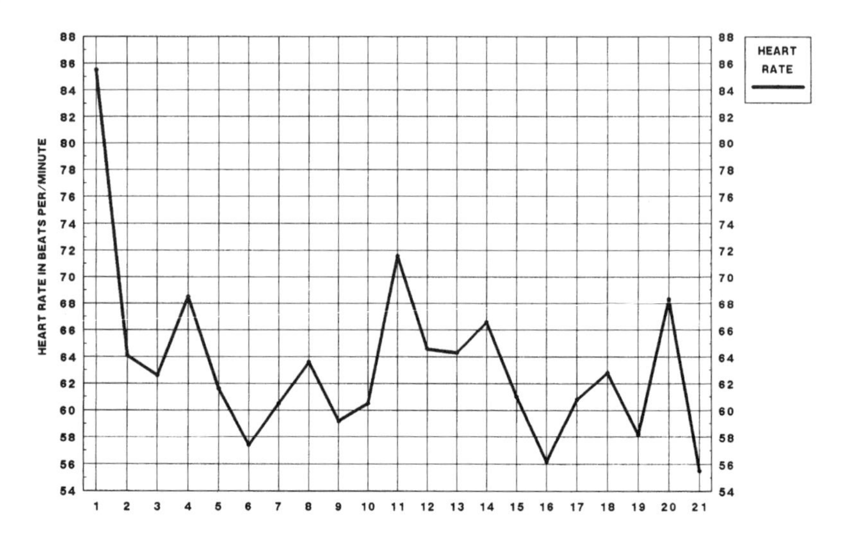

FIGURE 1.4A
Client A.A. heart rate measures across 21 sessions. Sensors measure heart rate (HR, wrist-to-wrist hookup, anterior surface) derived from an EKG measure.

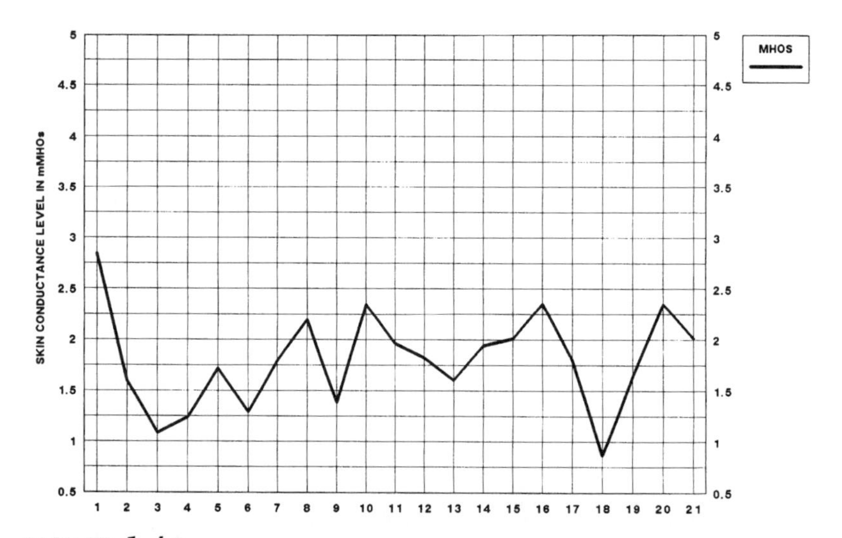

FIGURE 1.4B
Skin conductance level across 21 sessions (sensors placed on right hand, palmar surface of the index and second fingers).

The juggling act includes carrying on the elements of the treatment/training plan interventions, attending to the client's goals, and being receptive to new goals and possibilities along the way. It means that you are also concerned with the verbal communication. You are also aware and concerned about how the client is experiencing and responding to the experience. You are concerned with the instrumentation and whether it is giving valid information—whether it is free of artifacts. You are aware of the data and how they reflect the process. You are aware of your own behavior and what it is communicating—how it is impacting on the client. You are concerned to remain relaxed and to model the desired behavior.

CONGRUENCE IN THE BIOFEEDBACK THERAPIST

"Congruence" refers to the degree to which the therapist, in this case a biofeedback therapist/trainer, is consistent in behavior. This consistency includes what the trainer says, and his or her behaviors (physiological state, gestures, facial expressions, and so forth). The biofeedback trainer must maximize the "experimenter effect" (the effect that the experimenter/trainer has on the outcome) by modeling relaxation, well-being, homeostasis, and the like, and fostering that state in the interaction. That is one of the reasons why training with a personal trainer is emphasized. Biofeedback therapy can be seen as a special instance of Rogerian client-centered work, developed by Carl Rogers, in which the therapist practices unconditional positive regard for the client. The biofeedback therapist must be very congruent. Extensive biofeedback training of the biofeedback therapist increases congruence and effective functioning.

HIPPOCRATIC OATH

The biofeedback practitioner, aided by the ethical code, needs to take a kind of Hippocratic oath. He or she needs to vow not to harm clients and to help in whatever way possible. This means that the therapist does not rob you of autonomy, but as much as possible gives you the capacity to solve problems and practice self-regulation. The practitioner gives you information and sources for additional information, encouraging the idea that you can be self-responsible.

I believe that the biofeedback practitioner needs to make a commitment that is not unlike the doctor's Hippocratic oath, or even the commitment to priesthood. The biofeedback practitioner needs to commit to following an ethical code, to healthful living in his or her own life, and to a sense of "self-less" service.

THE WOUNDED HEALER

The biofeedback practitioner has often gone through an illness and has found a cure or management of the condition through biofeedback and self-regulation. Some of the best practitioners have had such experiences. This adds to their conviction about the importance of self-healing and wellness. They communicate that conviction more fully than if their realization of the role of self-healing in wellness had been more of a passive, third-person experience. However, practitioners need to be careful not to impose on their clients the strategies that they have found to be valuable for themselves.

PRACTITIONER AS MODEL

It is very important for the biofeedback practitioner to model the principles that are being taught. This means that you as a practitioner must maintain your own health. You must also engage in ongoing self-regulation as a means of self-care. This discipline must be a functioning, integrated part of your life. Since I have had contact with biofeedback practitioners over the years, I have been impressed by the degree to which it becomes an integral part of their lives. They tend to use biofeedback regularly in their lives, integrating it into their lifestyles, with their families and friends. They share their insights with others in an informal, natural way. This does not mean that the people with whom you share your information will be able to apply it immediately. Sometimes they can, but they may only be able to grasp it at some later point. Perhaps you will be able to see their activity coming from the seeds you have planted.

HOLISM

At its best, the biofeedback process is holistic, meaning that it brings together elements from your body, mind, and spirit. Spirit is defined as "the immaterial intelligent or sentient part of a person" (*Webster's Ninth New Collegiate Dictionary,* 1987). In much of biofeedback, the spiritual element is a byproduct that becomes richer as psychophysiological control is gained. For example, with biofeedback training the client may spontaneously mention a desire to learn meditation or express a renewed appreciation for a spiritual tradition with which he or she is familiar. The client may also label the biofeedback experience as spiritual even in a primarily non-spiritual setting. Some people working on this specifically are aware of this as a "main treatment effect."

MIND/BODY INTEGRATION

Biofeedback is seen as one of the tools for increasing mind/body integration and manipulation. Biofeedback seen in this light is truly living up to its early potential as described by the article originally titled, "Evolution by Prosthesis" (Ezios, 1971). This is biofeedback in a whole different partnership; it is really the augmentation of perceptual modes so that the new information can enable you to accomplish a whole new level of integration, moving from the "old"-brain, reflexive level to the "new"-brain, higher level of organization.

LEARNING, MEMORY, AND COGNITION

There are different theories as to how learning occurs neurologically. Some of the current research includes the notion that it involves activity of the hippocampus, protein synthesis and actual structural changes in the brain. This is important in the consideration of biofeedback because what you want to have happen is a relatively permanent change in behavior. You hope that the client will be able to function differently in the world, with greater health and comfort. Biofeedback learning includes repetition and the utilization of the neural circuits involved. There are also insights that come from the process, insights about how you are functioning and how you might be more effective. Repeated physiological training gradually shapes the new organization of your psychophysiology so that you use the new organizational patterns while engaging in tasks. The results of the learning are conscious and unconscious.

For many years we have been tracking the location of memory. There have been different theories as to where memory is located in the brain. About twenty years ago there was a happy discovery, in the work of Wilder Penfield, that stimulating certain areas of the brain during surgery yielded an experience of a memory. Restimulation of the area gave the same memory. It was as if you were experiencing the patient's scenario overlaid on top of the actual experiences. So for a time we thought we had found the location of memory: the temporal lobe. This discovery was communicated far and wide. It was in all the textbooks. Then they discovered in subsequent studies that if you changed the patient's mental state, a new memory was stimulated. So the area is involved in memory, but not discretely stored there.

PASSIVE VOLITION

A valuable learning from biofeedback is passive volition. Passive volition refers to the self-regulation of a physiological function in a passive way, through allowing or enabling oneself to make the change. This is different from our usual approach to things. We usually engage in active volition—we decide to do something and then make ourselves do it.

The practice of passive volition is valuable in its own right. Many of our life experiences go better when approached from a more passive volitional perspective, using just the right amount of energy and effort, remaining relaxed and poised. So in doing biofeedback practice, our behavior is shaped until we are more comfortable approaching a task in that way. This style or approach, passive volition, generalizes to other situations.

CHAPTER TWO

STIMULATION, AROUSAL, ADAPTATION LEVEL

"In addition to the EEG changes that mark intense excitation of the RAS, referred to as the arousal pattern, psychologists (e.g., Duffy 1957, Malmo 1957) are beginning to recognize the degree of arousal as a dimension or continuum, as one of the variables that would have to be assigned a value if the psychological condition of a human being or higher animal at any particular time were to be adequately described. It is a measure of how wide awake the organism is, of how ready it is to react. The lower pole of the continuum is represented by sleep or coma, while the upper pole would be reached in states of frantic excitement."

D. E. BERLYNE

"Biofeedback training has been a very valuable tool for self-awareness. In an existential sense, it provides me with a greater sensitivity to my internal processes in the moment and, thus, facilitates the opportunity to self-adjust my psychophysiology."

JOHN GINGRICH, BIOFEEDBACKER

This chapter will present a framework for understanding the changes that biofeedback and adjunctive procedures provide.

STIMULATION

We live in an ocean of stimulation. A stimulus is a change in the environment that impacts on us, causing physiological change. A stimulus is a form of energy, and energy is defined as the capacity to do work. There are different forms of energy—kinetic, potential, chemical, etc. It can be considered a stimulus for an organism when it is perceived and causes a response.

We are continually bombarded by changes in energy. Pressure changes of sound impact on us from head to toe. Our skin is our largest sense organ and it is continually responding to the vibrations of sound, just as our auditory system responds to sound. Our skin comes from the same embryonic layer as our nervous system.

As we experience the world, the stimulation of the environment differentially impacts on our sensory receptors. We sort out the impact according to the kind of stimulation impacting on the particular kind of sensory receptor. For example, photons of light energy are processed by retinal (back of the eye) cells. The kind of energy provided by the stimulus is transduced (transformed) by the sensory receptor cell. The transduction process converts it into another form of energy, which is conducted through the central nervous system in the form of electrochemical impulses to the area of the brain that is responsible for processing it, e.g., the visual process is conducted to the occipital lobe and superior colliculi. Therefore, we convert environmental experiences into electrochemical impulses.

We need this stimulation in order to keep our organism functioning and intact. Evidence from astronauts experiencing zero gravity shows us some of the effects of removing part of our habitual stimulus input. Evidence from osteoporosis changes in elderly women shows us how necessary it is that we receive the stimulation of exercise and walking in order to maintain skeletal integrity.

We are the result of our cellular interactions and responses to the environment. From the very beginning, there has been an interaction between our genetic blueprint and the impact of the environment. The results of our interactions and responses are programmed into our organisms.

We need environmental stimulation as much as we need the food that we eat. In part, we need the demands of the environment to tell us where to put the nutrients and energy that we consume.

AROUSAL CONTINUUM

During the day, we move up and down an arousal continuum (Figure 2.1). Although it is not a unitary continuum (the arousal of the system as a whole), we might look at it this way for a bit. We can use this concept to form a mental image, which can serve as a metaphor to help us understand a very complicated process.

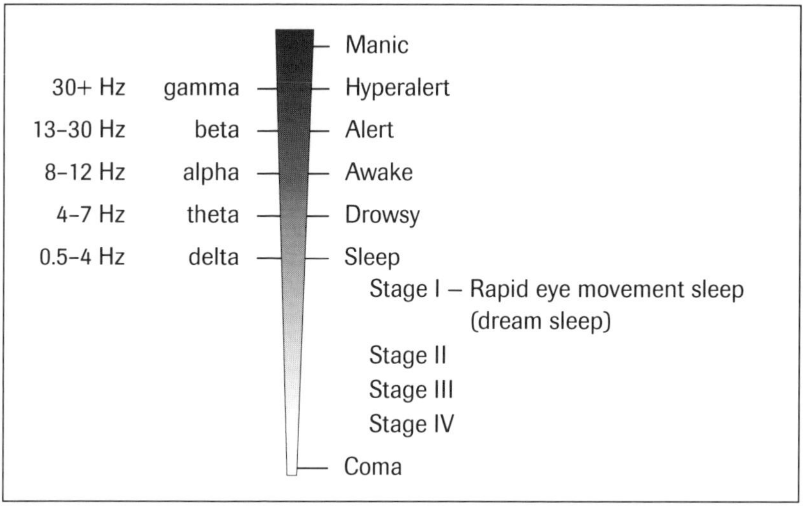

Manic
30+ Hz gamma — Hyperalert
13–30 Hz beta — Alert
8–12 Hz alpha — Awake
4–7 Hz theta — Drowsy
0.5–4 Hz delta — Sleep
Stage I – Rapid eye movement sleep (dream sleep)
Stage II
Stage III
Stage IV
Coma

FIGURE 2.1
Level of arousal and consciousness associated with brain waves.

The arousal continuum extends from coma through mania. The different levels may be seen as coma, the four levels of sleep and rapid eye movement sleep, drowsiness, awakeness, alertness, hyperalertness, and mania. If we use the activity of occipital EEG, we can correlate brain waves (cycles-per-second or Hertz) to these levels. Coma is somewhat flat and irregular. Deep sleep is delta (0–3 Hz); drowsiness is theta (4–7 Hz); the waking brain wave pattern is alpha (8–13 Hz); alertness is beta (14–30 Hz); and more than 30 Hz is hyperalert.

These brain wave levels correspond to activation of the other physiological systems, which include parasympathetic activity (Figure 2.2) up through the state of alertness. At the alert levels we may see increases in sympathetic nervous system (SNS) activity (Figure 2.2). Individuals respond with different patterns of nervous system mobilization. Some people fractionate. Fractionation is a term used to describe physiological systems activating in patterns that are not consistent with the situation at hand. For example, the skin temperature may go up while the electrodermal response (EDR) also goes up. Ordinarily, we would expect the skin temperature to go up while the EDR lowers. We all fractionate from time to time, based on the situation and our prior learnings.

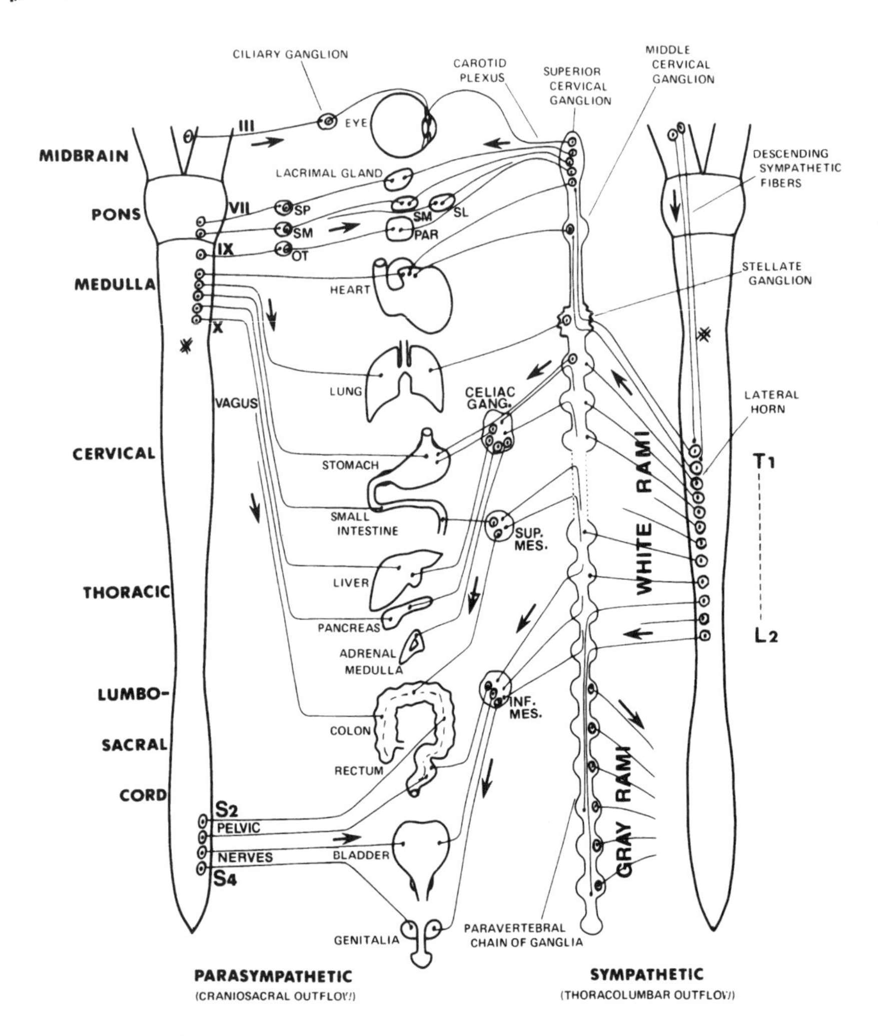

FIGURE 2.2
The parasympathetic and sympathetic nervous systems.

As brain waves move up the arousal continuum and you become more aroused, there is a shift from homeostasis or parasympathetic nervous system dominance to sympathetic nervous system dominance. Characteristic changes of the sympathetic nervous system accompany this process. These changes include increased heart rate; increased blood pressure; increased blood flow to the brain, spinal cord and muscles; decreased gastrointestinal activity; decreased blood clotting time; eccrine gland secretion; increased muscle tone; pupil dilation; and brain wave shift to beta—all parts of the preparation for fighting or running (the fight-or-flight response). Activation of the sympathetic nervous system (SNS) continues until the factors causing the increased arousal decrease or the person becomes habituated.

SLEEP AND AROUSAL

In biofeedback training, you are learning to self-regulate your levels of arousal so that you can better match the situation at hand. This means that you are more clearly alert when it is time to be alert; you are more clearly ready for sleep when it is time to go to sleep. You might say that there is less "noise" in your system: less extraneous physiological activity interfering with your capacity to achieve the desired state. For example, when you lie down to sleep you do not lie there for an extended period of time with your musculature overly contracted, feeding the activity level into the RAS to activate the brain.

RETICULAR ACTIVATING SYSTEM (RAS)

The reticular activating system (RAS) is a network of fibers passing through the brain stem to and from the brain (Figure 2.3). Actually, it is axons of neurons passing through the anterior portion of the brain stem. The neural pathways conduct ascending sensory input to the brain and descending impulses to the muscles. The ascending impulses alert the brain by way of the diffuse thalamic activating system; the descending impulses cause the gamma motor systems in the muscles to increase muscle tone, the resting contraction level.

The RAS is necessary for alertness and attention. Changes in sensory input to the RAS determine our level of arousal, alertness, and attention.

ORIENTING REFLEX

When something changes in the environment (a new stimulus), there is an orienting response or reflex (OR). Originally described by Ivan Pavlov, the orienting reflex is a brief sympathetic nervous system discharge. The purpose of the response is to orient toward a change in the environmental stimulation and prepare to deal with it.

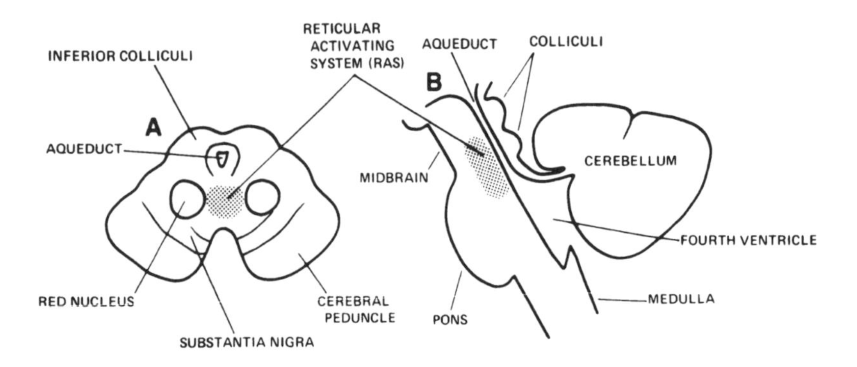

FIGURE 2.3
The reticular activating system (RAS) viewed in the transverse (A) and midsagittal (B) sections of the brainstem.

There are a number of physiological changes that accompany the OR. They include change of brain waves to beta (13–30 Hz), and shift of blood flow from the periphery to the muscles and brain. This is a brief response. When the stimulus is processed and determined to be non-threatening, habituation occurs.

All of this is referred to as the orienting reflex. It was discovered by Ivan Pavlov, and further developed by E. N. Sokolov. The response involves a shift toward SNS dominance, the fight-or-flight system. It prepares a person to fight or run.

The orienting response habituates quickly. Therefore, the person quickly checks out the stimulus, and upon determining its nature, begins to shift back toward homeostasis and increased parasympathetic nervous system (PNS) activity.

HABITUATION

Habituation is the term used to describe what happens when a stimulus is presented over and over. Eventually, the person ceases to respond physiologically. Habituation is a primitive form of learning.

ADAPTATION LEVEL

When stimulation is prolonged, we adapt to the stimulus. This means that our response to the stimulus decreases. Adaptation level is a concept developed by Harry Helson and others in the 1940s (Helson, 1947). It refers to the adaptation of an organism to the current environmental stimulation. If one changes the level of stimulation a little, the result may be pleasurable. This is true whether it is an increase or decrease in stimulation. If the change is greater, the result is painful.

When one moves into a new environment with a difference in stimulation level, a process of adaptation takes place. It takes about six months to adapt to a large change in one's life. If there are complicating factors, it might take longer. For example, the loss of a loved one may take one and a half to two years, or longer.

OPTIMAL PERFORMANCE

The inverted-U of the relationship between level of arousal and performance was discovered by Yerkes and Dodson (1908)—the Yerkes-Dodson law (Figure 2.4). The X axis relates to the level of arousal and the Y axis is concerned with the level of performance. As the level of arousal increases, performance increases to a certain point, and then declines with additional arousal. What this means is that as arousal levels increase, the person is more effective until the arousal level becomes counterproductive. Theoretically, there is an optimal level of arousal for every task. From amphetamine/performance studies in the 1960s, we see that simple gross motor tasks are performed more efficiently with greater activation, while performance of intellectual or fine motor tasks suffers with such activation. A classic story of the student who took amphetamines before an essay exam, wrote furiously during the exam, and was found to have written everything on one line of the bluebook, is an example.

RESEARCH IN BIOFEEDBACK

Research in biofeedback is similar to research in other areas of psychology. The investigator selects a population, the group to whom he or she would like to generalize the results. Then the investigator randomly selects a subset of the target population, called the sample. The sample needs to mirror as closely as possible the characteristics of the larger population, because generalizations from the research can only be made to a population that resembles the sample. If you choose a sample of college sophomores from a particular college, as so many psychology studies have, you would be able to generalize your findings to people of similar characteristics—college sophomores from a demographically similar college.

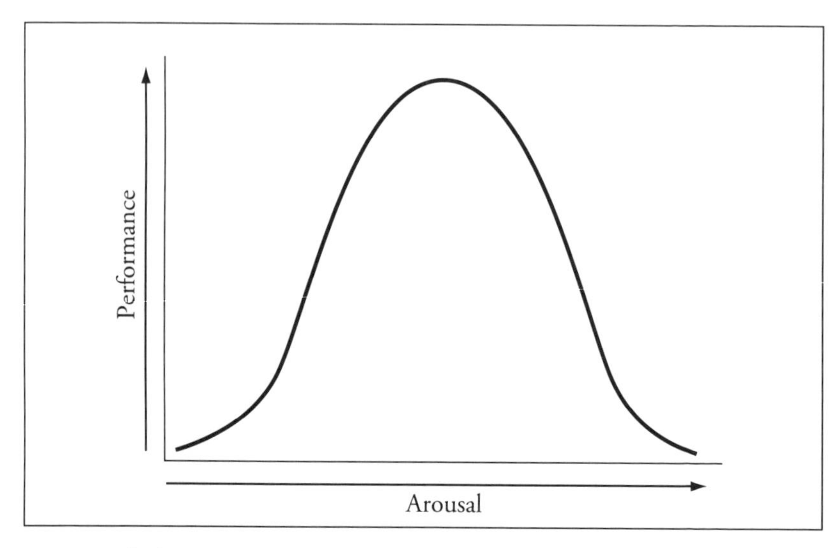

FIGURE 2.4
Inverted-U of arousal versus performance, after the Yerkes-Dobson Law.

You might want to be able to generalize your results to migraine headache sufferers. Since you cannot measure the response of all possible migraine headache sufferers, you would select a subset of the migraine headache population as the sample. In medical and psychophysiological research, it is common to have a sample size that is relatively small compared to sample sizes in other areas of human research. The reason for this is often the difficulty of getting a large number of people with the medical condition in question, or the expense (time, labor, resources) of the research protocol. In contrast, a paper and pencil test used with a group of people can measure large numbers without a great deal of time and expense.

A sample is selected from the population using the random number process, in the hope that the sample is reasonably representative of the population (not biased). The more idiosyncratic the sample, the less reasonable it is to generalize the findings to the population in question.

The randomly selected sample is randomly placed in at least two groups: an experimental group and a control group. The experimental group is the group with which the experimenter will vary some of the procedure. The control group (there are various kinds of control groups, including waiting lists, nonspecific treatment groups, etc.) is given an alternative experience that does not include the "active ingredient" or specific treatment. The pre- and post-experimental treatment measures are compared for both groups. There are other combinations of control groups, but this is a simple research design.

The experiment has at least one independent variable and a dependent variable. The independent variable is the element that the experimenter will vary or manipulate. The dependent variable is an element that varies because of the changes in the independent variable. For example, in a biofeedback study the independent variable might be a particular biofeedback training protocol. The dependent variable might be the physiological measures in the pre- and post-baseline recordings or a symptom log. Hopefully, the dependent variable is subject to the effects of the independent variable.

Dependent variables are measured before and after the experimental treatment. Dependent variables differ from study to study and within research traditions. Dependent variables include paper and pencil tests, global observations by trained judges, psychophysiological measures, projective tests, interviews, etc.

A simple research design includes:

R01	X	02	(experimental group)
R03		04	(control group)

This means that the groups are randomly (R) assigned to the experimental and control groups. Then they are observed using the selected approach to measuring the dependent variable. In the case of biofeedback training, the dependent variable may be baseline data on a particular biofeedback modality such as electromyograph (EMG) μV level and/or symptom occurrence measures. Then the experimental treatment is provided to the experimental group. In biofeedback, this might be a series of biofeedback training sessions, perhaps with selected adjunctive procedures. In the hypothetical case above, the adjunctive procedures might be progressive relaxation suggestions.

As a biofeedback practitioner, you need to consider yourself a clinician-researcher. The work that you do is an experiment, whether you are aware of it or not. Your client comes to you with a problem or goal. You will assess the situation and develop a hypothesis about what might be effective with your client's presenting problem or goal. Your assessment will include taking a thorough psychosocial and medical history and baseline measures in the appropriate feedback modalities. These measures are dependent variables. Some of these dependent variables will, you hope, be altered by the treatment/training intervention(s) you choose. Then you will develop a treatment/training plan, which may be modified by the biofeedback series; it will represent the independent variable or variables. The client will be varying or changing the experience by adding or subtracting elements from his or her life.

For example, you may have the client relax at home using appropriate techniques that have been shown to be effective in the lab. You may also have the client practice one or more adjunctive procedures during the day on a daily basis. As you move through training, you will be observing brief baseline recordings as you begin your sessions. You will also take post-baseline readings during the termination phase.

You will evaluate, formally or informally, the effectiveness of your interventions. Is there a difference between pre- and post-training baselines as seen on the biofeedback instruments? Is there a difference between symptom ratings (frequency, intensity, or duration), or behaviors (presence of health- or performance-promoting behaviors or absence of health- or performance-compromising behaviors)? You may pay very close attention to this single case study or you may treat the data as clinical information that is passed on to the client and perhaps to some degree to the referring physician or other concerned and appropriate referral source.

ARTIFACTS IN BIOFEEDBACK RESEARCH

The artifacts in biofeedback research include: investigator and experimenter as sources of bias, demand characteristics, subject roles, sensitization effects, response biases, and subject-selection biases. The investigator is the person who plans the study. The experimenter runs the study, working with the subjects. In the case of biofeedback training, the experimenter is the biofeedback practitioner. The investigator/experimenter effect is the impact of some quality of the investigator/experimenter on the subject, and it may help create an effect separate from the specific treatment effect. For example, the investigator/experimenter might be a warm, encouraging person around whom people have a tendency to relax. This would be a confounding variable.

In the clinical setting, you are concerned with removing variables that might interfere with clients learning the biofeedback skills, but in the lab setting you are trying to determine whether biofeedback alone or as part of a treatment package is efficacious in its own right.

EVALUATING RESEARCH IN BIOFEEDBACK

It is necessary to evaluate research as you read it and to decide whether to utilize the findings in your own work. When you read the findings of research, sometimes the bottom line is what stands out. We often find the conclusions from a study presented in newspaper headlines, or perhaps they appear in the title of a magazine article, such as one that appeared in *Psychology Today* a few years ago indicating that biofeedback did not work.

Sometimes people, other professionals or clients or even friends, will make a statement to the effect that biofeedback doesn't work. In a visit to Australia years ago, I met this attitude based on conclusions from American research at the time. The rumor had spread, from articles in magazines and journals, that biofeedback was not "efficacious" or effective. This posed a problem for me because I was there to teach people how to use biofeedback. With additional research, these attitudes have changed.

When people come to you with criticisms of biofeedback, you need to be able to discuss the criticisms with them intelligently. If you have a copy of the article in question, you can review it to see what the nature of the criticism is and on what it is based. If you are confronted with the person and no article, you will have to question him or present more generic explanations of the difficulties in doing valid research.

In psychological research and related health care fields, certain standards of research have been accepted by the professional community. They have been developed over the years and are the traditions of that research history. One of the characteristic elements of psychological research is that it begins with observations, either naturalistic observations of behavior or the results of previous studies. These observations lead to certain hunches about the phenomenon. The hunches lead to the formation of hypotheses.

Hypotheses are statements about behavior. They are stated in the null, or negative, perspective. The concept behind this is that since you do not have complete information, you can at least speculate that your intervention will have no effect. If it does have an effect, the null hypothesis is rejected and the alternate hypothesis is accepted.

STANDARD RESEARCH DESIGN

The biofeedback process follows a somewhat standard research design. The client comes in, and through the initial evaluation or intake interview presents the problem (called the presenting complaint or presenting problem). This is analogous to the observation phase of research.

The assessment is made, which includes the hypothesis that biofeedback would be an appropriate intervention. (The client may come with this hypothesis, or be referred by a physician.)

DEMAND CHARACTERISTICS OF THE BIOFEEDBACK ENVIRONMENT

Demand characteristics of an environment refer to the various factors within the environment that promote certain behaviors. For example, the biofeedback lab may be arranged in such a way as to facilitate relaxation. There may be a large, comfortable recliner chair. You may actually recline the chair for the client. The lights are usually incandescent and low in intensity. Often the room is in a quiet area. There may be pleasant objects in the room, such as pictures and other items. The colors may be relatively quiet, and the arrangement of furniture designed to be as soothing as possible. Many of these elements may suggest calm, soothing physiological responses.

The actual hookup procedure may also be soothing. Fairly routine movements such as cleaning the skin, attaching the electrodes, plugging in the electrode cable, etc., may be soothing in their own unique way. All of these maneuvers and elements may suggest a psychophysiological state and mood to the subject. These suggestions are separate from the actual specific treatment, biofeedback training. If the client is a trained meditator, for instance, the situation may prompt a relaxation response even without the biofeedback stimulus. In fact, the biofeedback stimulus may be a distraction for some people who are used to eliciting the relaxation response without feedback signals.

PLACEBO EFFECT

The word "placebo" comes from the Latin, meaning "to please." The placebo effect takes place, for example, in drug studies when some subjects do not receive active medication (the control group), but do receive inert substances. It also occurs when doctors prescribe certain medications to patients. You can look at this effect in two ways. The doctor has pleased the patient by giving some sort of medication, although it was not a specific treatment for the complaint. The patient pleased the doctor by complying with the suggestion that medication was given and recovery should follow. For many years, it was considered that those who exhibited the placebo effect were very suggestible people, who simply used their imaginations. In recent years, though, research has shown that an actual physiological change occurs. With the suggestion element of the medication, good subjects are able to mobilize their physiologies to foster the healing, pain-relieving process. Studies have shown that naloxone can counteract the pain-relieving effect of placebo pain management (it cannot knock out hypnosis-based pain relief, however).

In biofeedback research, you are interested in finding the true active ingredient in the process. You are interested in removing placebo effect elements. In clinical biofeedback, you are interested in mobilizing every aspect of the patient/client's healing process, and whatever placebo factors are operating are welcome. Therefore, you want to line up all elements within the situation so that they help foster the attitude of healing, hope, physiological homeostasis, etc.

This chapter has explored the nature of stimulation of our environment (internal and external), our responses to environmental stimulation (arousal), adaptation level (the level of environmental stimulation to which we are adapted), and the nature of biofeedback research.

CHAPTER THREE

BIOFEEDBACK AND SOMATICS

"SOMATICS (so•ma'•tiks) n. pl. (construed as singular). 1. The art and science of the inter-relational process between awareness, biological function and environment, all three factors being understood as a synergistic whole: the field of somatics. 2. The study of the soma, soma being the biological body of functions by which and through which awareness and environment are mediated. It is understood that the word soma *designates any living organism, animal or plant. It is also understood that all such somas have, to some degree, the capacity for awareness (sensorium) of the environment and intentional action (motorium) in the environment. 3. In common usage* somatics *relates to somas of the human species, whose sensoria and motoria are relatively free from the determination of genetically fixed behavior patterns, thus allowing learning to determine the inter-relational process between awareness, biological function and environment. [Gk.* somatikos, soma, somat- *body. F.* somatique.*]"*

THOMAS HANNA

"I will continue my journey knowing that every movement that I do make will enhance my life. Periodically, I will challenge myself to try the others again. I have a feeling that once the SOMA gets a wake-up call, there is no limit to its potential. And by listening to my soul, I have discovered strength and courage that I did not know I had."

HELEN ELAINE, BIOFEEDBACKER

SOMATIC ASPECTS

The biofeedback process is for many people a first experience in the immediacy of the mind/body connection. Some people realize for the first time the extent of the impact that internal and external stimuli have on them. They find this frightening, and they may have some difficulty in accepting this realization. They may be tempted to deny the evidence. They may also show some brief recognition, which passes away quickly.

What keeps it from being quite so frightening is the realization that with this knowledge and skill we can make a big difference in what we allow to impact on us, and how we allow it. We begin to take this aspect of our lives into our own hands. We become, to an extent, masters of our fate, architects of our experiences and lives.

THE MIND/BODY UNIFIED STATE

The mind/body unified state has various advantages as a way of being in the world. It enables you to understand the impact of the environment on your physiology. With that awareness, you will be more careful about the impact of the environment on your being, and vice versa. Thus, through becoming more aware of the effect of your cognition and mental reactions on the environment, you gain some control over the environment and can decide the impact you want it to have.

SOMATICS AND BIOFEEDBACK

Somatics, a term developed by Thomas Hanna, is a field that addresses the unification of mind and body. Hanna begins with the concept of the "soma," which is the body experienced from within. ("Soma" is the Greek word for body. Historically, somatology was the name for the field that later was differentiated into anatomy and physiology. This differentiation served to separate the study of the structure of the body from the study of its functions.) From the perspective of Hanna's definition of the soma, there is no mind/body split. The soma is process, function rather than structure. It is the result of the original creation of the universe and the evolution over time to our current expression of that organic foundation (Hanna, 1980).

Somatics is concerned with the first-person versus the third-person perspective. Biofeedback is concerned with external, third-person information,

Photo by Joel Gordon

Thomas Hanna

but the information is finally used by the person from the first-person perspective.

Hanna identified three reflexes: the "Red Light," "Green Light," and "trauma" reflex (Figures 3.1A, 3.1B, 3.1C, and 3.1D). The concept of the Red Light reflex builds on Hans Selye's observations about the stress response, but presents the overall syndrome of changes of which it is a part. The Red Light reflex is also referred to as the "startle response" or the "escape response."

THE STARTLE REFLEX

The startle reflex (Figure 3.1A) is a set of changes that happen rapidly when there is a sudden change in the environmental stimulation. This might be a loud noise nearby or someone who says "Boo!" The reflex includes a set of reliably occurring responses such as eyes widening, muscles contracting, respiration stopping, etc. You take quite a while to return to baseline. In fact, with repeated triggering of the startle reflex, which Hanna calls the Red Light reflex, there will be some chronic muscular holdings.

The following quote is from Hanna's book *Somatics* (1988), in which he describes the Red Light reflex:

> All mammals that have been studied exhibit the withdrawal response. Even in these complex animals, the reflex is quick and effective. And in the most complex mammal, the human being, the withdrawal response is amazingly quick. If a woman walking down a street hears the sudden explosion of a car backfiring, this is what happens: Within 14 milliseconds the muscles of her jaw begin to contract; this is immediately followed about 20 milliseconds later by a contraction of her eyes and brow. But, before her eyes have squeezed shut, her shoulder and neck muscles (the trapezius) have received a neural impulse at 20 milliseconds to contract, raising her shoulders and bringing her head forward. At 60 milliseconds, her elbows bend, and then her hands begin to turn palms-downward. These descending neural impulses continue by contracting the abdominal muscle, which brings her trunk forward, simultaneously pulling down her rib cage and stopping her breathing. And, immediately after that, her knees bend and point inward, while her ankles roll her feet inward. The muscles of the crotch tighten, and the toes lift upward. This sums up the Red Light reflex—the body's withdrawal from danger. The body is flexed and crouched, almost as if ready to fall and curl up in a fetal posture (Eaton, 1984).
>
> This cascade of neural impulses begins in the face, then goes down to the neck, then to the arms and trunk, and, finally, to the legs and toes. Why this sequence from the head downwards? Because the impulse originates in the lower-level brain stem and arrives at the muscles of the head region earliest, taking time to travel down its pathways to the lower parts of the body.
>
> This withdrawal response, shared by humans with the rest of the animal kingdom, emanates from the primitive regions of the hindbrain—to be precise, from the reticulospinal tract originating from the ventral pontine and medullar reticular formation (Eaton, 1984). Thus, the mechanism of this reflex lies deep beneath the control of the forebrain where conscious, voluntary actions originate. Not only is the withdrawal reflex

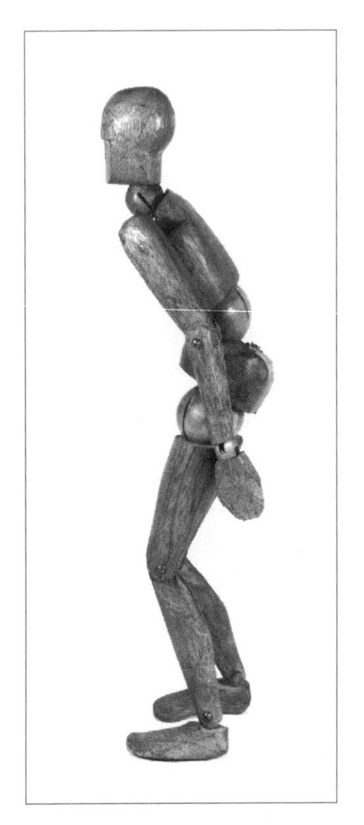

FIGURE 3.1A
Red Light reflex.

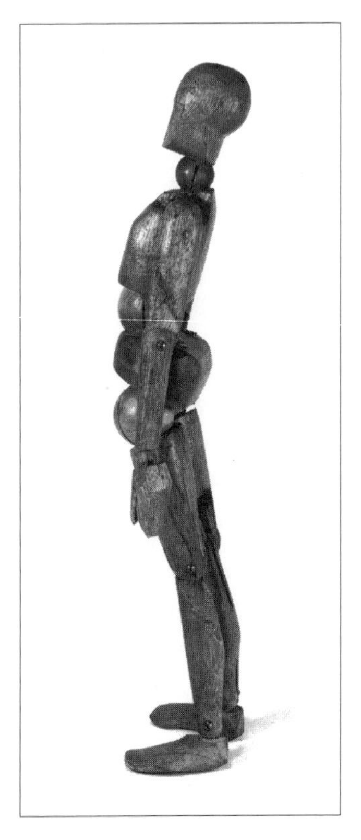

FIGURE 3.1B
Green Light reflex.

more primitive than our voluntary actions, it is much faster. It happens before we can consciously perceive or inhibit it. It is our primitive protector, whose motto is 'Withdraw now, and think about it later.' Survival demands an immediate response. We do not have the luxury to reflect at length on how dangerous the sudden threat really is.

The Green Light reflex refers to the postural reflex that begins around six months of age when the infant first contracts the back extensor muscles. This is called the Landau reflex and includes the arched back, extended neck, arms, and legs. It enables the infant to sit up and then stand in preparation for walking. It is the activation of our anti-gravity muscles. Some adults have habitu-

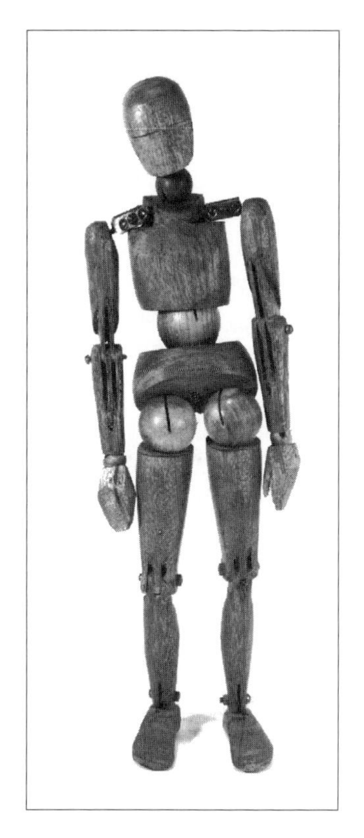

FIGURE 3.1C
Trauma reflex:
Simple scoliosis with C-curve.

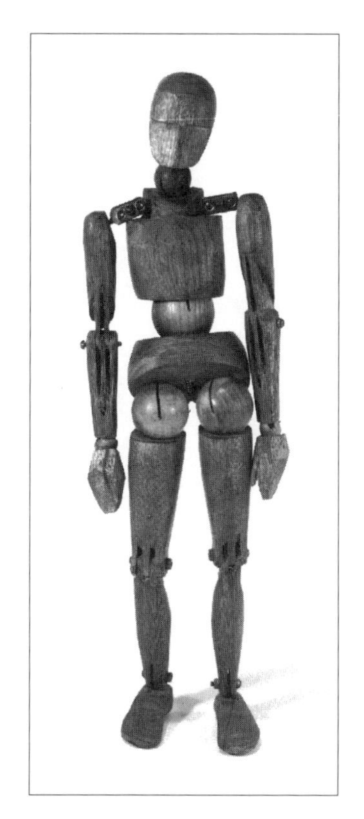

FIGURE 3.1D
Trauma reflex:
Scoliosis with S-curve.

ated into this posture (Figure 3.1B). EMG recordings of the muscles involved in this posture show elevated microvolt readings for the muscles listed above.

The trauma reflex (Figures 3.1C and 3.1D) includes motor contractions which surround any trauma—accident, surgery, long-term stress, etc. EMG feedback relates to it most specifically, but there are also other physiological changes which surround the protective stance or coping strategies.

Hanna also wrote about the "Dark Vise" in which the Red Light and Green Light reflexes operate simultaneously, holding the person in a tight postural configuration which he called the "senile posture" (Figure 3.2). These reflexes are valuable assessment templates for biofeedback.

FIGURE 3.2
Senile posture.

Thomas Hanna put forth the concept of sensory-motor amnesia (SMA) to describe the tendency of humans to forget certain movements or ways of relating to muscles or muscle groups, leaving them chronically contracted. The contraction is the result of ongoing brain stem-level impulses sent to the motor units, causing contractions of muscle fibers. The return to cortical control returns the control of the muscles to the client. This is true of the body systems as well: biofeedback enables us to gain or regain greater control with awareness and conscious self-regulation.

Somatic work (a kind of hands-on biofeedback) and biofeedback (instrument-based biofeedback) involve a shift from the reflexive, automatic physiological programs to the more voluntary control areas of the brain and behavior, involving more cortical control.

Somatic education is an educational experience in which the client is taught how to regain control of various muscle groups and movement patterns. Somatic education seeks to encourage the person to voluntarily contract certain muscle groups that may be in involuntary contraction due to some stimulus which has evoked a reflex contraction. This may become habitual. When a muscle is chronically contracted, it is not available for a new contraction. It is fatigued; its motor units are already in constant involvement. Therefore, it is necessary to get the muscle to relax. Muscles are relaxed by the cortex inhibition of the flow of impulses to the muscles.

It is important for us to realize that in biofeedback we are dealing with the brain and related nervous systems. We are also dealing with areas of the brain of which we are not aware, but which are just as significant in controlling behavior. We are concerned with shifting areas of brain control.

When considering biofeedback and somatics, it is helpful to use Carl Jung's concept of the "Self," which is the center of the conscious and unconscious mind. We are not able to know it directly, but in such processes as dreams and other glimpses, we get to know the greater wisdom that the overview of our Self has of us and our lives. I like to think that biofeedback enables us to get a sense of that organizing center, which has enormous wisdom to offer.

There are many approaches to somatics. Any practice that includes mind/body integration as a focus can be considered somatic. These approaches include Eastern and Western traditions. Examples of Eastern traditions include martial arts disciplines, yoga, zen, t'ai chi, Tibetan Buddhist practices, and many others. Western traditions include the Alexander Technique, Feldenkrais™, Functional Integration™ and Awareness through Movement™, Somatic Exercises™ by Thomas Hanna, Ida Rolf's Structural Integration and related methods, somatically oriented dance and athletics, massage therapy, biofeedback training, and many other disciplines. Medicine, chiropractic, physical therapy, psychotherapy, and other disciplines may be considered somatic when they integrate mind and body.

FUTURE OF THE BODY

Michael Murphy has put together a monumental work, entitled *The Future of the Body* (1992). The implications of the evidence that he has been gathering from many sources are astonishing: that humans are capable of being more flexibly connected in an embodied way; that we may achieve enhanced capabilities, ways of working with our world; that we are capable of bodily change as orchestrated by mental change; and much more.

PSYCHOPHYSICAL HEALTH

I have come to believe that psychophysical health is the most important aspect of our lives. It needs to be a central focus. From this can evolve a concern for the welfare of others and of the environment. Unless you can care enough to provide self-care for yourself, you will not be able to care for others for as long.

I come to this realization from a lifetime of concern for others at the expense of myself. I learned this from the modeling of my mother, a very self-sacrificing person, and my basic temperament, which is extraverted. Extraversion is a term coined by Carl Jung to describe the character of a person who regulates his or her behavior according to how it will impact on others.

METAVIEW

Biofeedback training and somatics encourage you to adopt a metaview of your physiological functions. Such a metaview is very helpful, and develops as you and your trainer look at how you are functioning psychophysiologically in a particular situation. Not only do you reflect on what is going on, but you may even reflect on this reflection. This means that instead of being submerged in the experience, you gain a new perspective on it, one of asserting some control over physiological function. You are observing yourself functioning, almost as you might do in a lucid dream. (In a lucid dream the dreamer is aware of herself dreaming and may even institute some changes in the dream based on that awareness.)

SHAMANISTIC HEALING

In the shamanistic concept of the healing process, one asks, what is needed to move the person back into balance and harmony is his life and in the environment? In what way is the person off course? What is he leaving out of his life? What potential is not being actualized?

In the relaxation process that accompanies biofeedback, there can be a turning towards receptivity of messages from within ourselves as to where we have been, what our experiences mean in the course of total life development, and where we might be going. There is a great relief in getting a sense of meaning of life experiences and direction.

A sense of purpose is an important buffer against stress; it is very valuable to have a sense of purpose during life events.

In conclusion, biofeedback and somatics are valuable tools for teaching self-regulation and self-responsibility. The shift from third-person control to first-person control of psychophysiology has profound implications for human functioning and development.

CHAPTER FOUR

INDICATIONS FOR BIOFEEDBACK

"Teaching patients to control a wide range of physiological processes occasionally has amazing therapeutic results . . . . True clinical biofeedback has quietly taken a place as a genuine treatment for a growing number of neurological and psychosomatic ailments."

JOHN V. BASMAJIAN

"Learning about the various applications of biofeedback training (skin temperature training, EDR, EMG, EEG) has allowed me to realize and use conscious control over my body. I can now monitor and modify my reactions to different situations and stimuli. This is very helpful in limiting and eliminating stress factors."

BRIDGET JOHNSON, BIOFEEDBACKER

When do you use biofeedback? Biofeedback is chosen as the appropriate intervention after a thorough assessment/evaluation (Figures 4.1, 4.2, and 4.3). This assessment is usually begun in the first telephone interview, during which you gather information to help you decide whether the person may be a good candidate for biofeedback. His or her verbal description of the presenting complaint or problem, prior experience with therapeutic interventions, and general situation will give you some initial idea about whether to see this client. Steve Fahrion, a psychologist at the Menninger Foundation, says to broaden your conception of who you might see until there is evidence that the client cannot

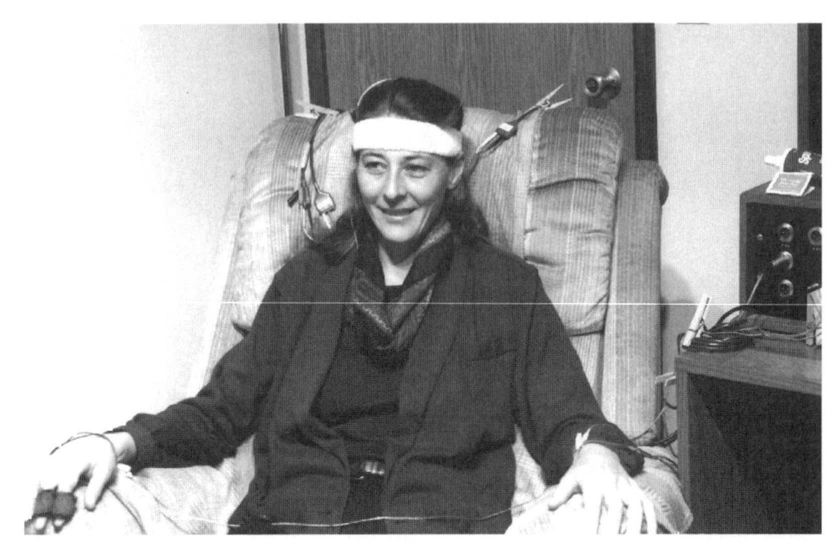

FIGURE 4.1
Client experiencing biofeedback. (Katee Wynia)

FIGURE 4.2
Stephen E. Wall facilitating biofeedback session.

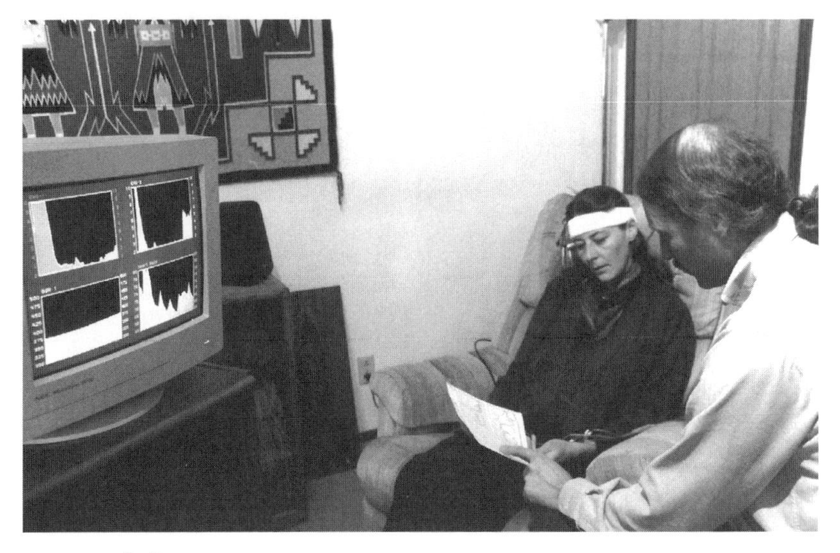

FIGURE 4.3
Stephen E. Wall discussing data with Katee Wynia.

benefit from biofeedback. In deciding when biofeedback is indicated, it becomes very important to do a thorough intake interview during the first visit.

Applications of biofeedback fall into several categories: medical, psychological, physical therapy, educational, business and industry, the arts, and sports.

Biofeedback modalities used for these applications are electroencephalograph feedback (EEG), electromyograph feedback (EMG), electrodermal activity (EDA) or galvanic skin response (GSR), and skin temperature training (ST). Different biofeedback modalities measure the activity of different nervous systems (Figure 4.4).

MEDICAL APPLICATIONS

Asthma Asthma, a chronic lung condition in which the bronchioles constrict, has been treated with biofeedback. EEG, EMG, and skin temperature training have been used with asthma clients. In addition, guided imagery has been used, utilizing such images as the lungs as an upside-down tree with its leaves and branches spread wide. Biofeedback with persons who experience

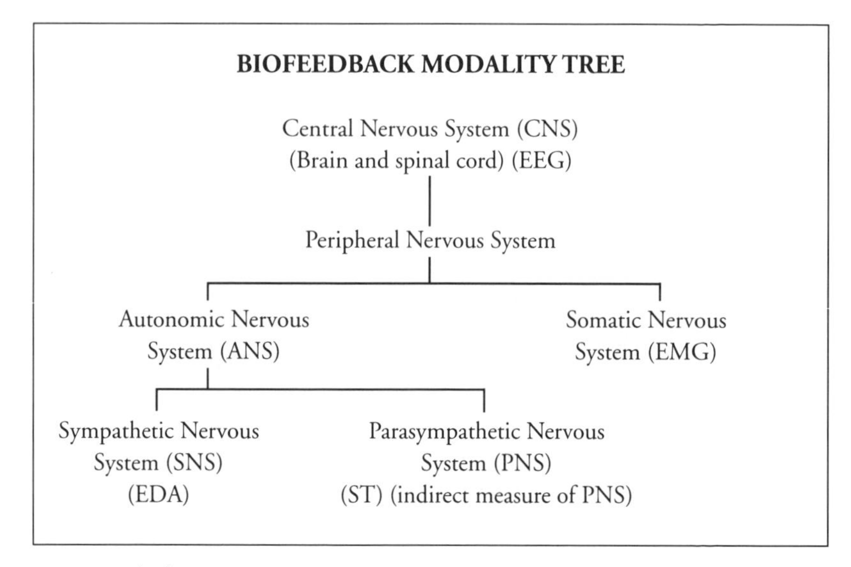

FIGURE 4.4
Biofeedback modality tree. The nervous systems and biofeedback modalities typically used to measure them.

asthma episodes emphasizes learning the relaxation response as a preventive measure. During an asthma episode, relaxation exercises are contraindicated. This is because the bronchioles have already contracted and you do not want to increase that tendency.

During the asthma episode, what is needed is a sympathetic nervous system outflow, which sometimes is encouraged by a sympathetic drug that mimics SNS activity. During sympathetic nervous system dominance, the bronchioles expand. During the asthma episode, the individual needs maximum oxygen, whereas during the relaxation response the bronchioles constrict.

You can use biofeedback to help the client explore his or her environment for stressors that seem to correlate with asthma episodes, and to help him or her maintain a basal level of relaxation to make it less likely that an asthma episode will occur. Biofeedback can also help the client be more comfortable taking his or her medication. There are a host of other peripheral benefits of the training experience. Biofeedback training has been reported to decrease the frequency of asthma episodes.

Essential and Labile Hypertension Hypertension is high blood pressure. Essential hypertension is high blood pressure for which there is no known structural cause. Labile hypertension is high blood pressure that fluctuates over time. If there is no structural cause for hypertension, then the individual may be able to learn how to control it. How is this possible? When the sympathetic nervous system is dominant, impulses go out along the SNS pathways, causing constriction of the peripheral blood vessels—contracting the smooth muscles of the blood vessels. This causes a redirection of blood flow from the peripheral blood vessels to those serving the brain and muscles. With the decrease in radius of the blood vessels, there is an increase in resistance to blood flow. There are other factors contributing to the increase in blood pressure, but this is a graphic example of how stress and a learned state of physiological tension might affect blood pressure on an ongoing, situational basis.

EMG feedback training was the original biofeedback approach for hypertension. Currently, the protocol developed by Steve Fahrion of the Menninger Foundation, which uses temperature training of the hands to criterion (95 degrees Fahrenheit) and then the feet, has been quite effective. Temperature training is used to decrease sympathetic nervous system outflow and thus to allow the blood vessels to dilate. Respiration training has also been used.

Insomnia Insomnia has been worked with using EEG biofeedback (alpha and theta frequency training). There are two kinds of insomnia: sleep onset insomnia and the kind in which you wake up in the middle of the night and are unable to go to sleep again. This is essentially an arousal response following a dream period (or REM—rapid eye movement—period). Every 90 minutes throughout the night we enter a period of REM sleep. EEG training for insomnia teaches the person to shift brain waves and thus the arousal level of the brain in the direction toward sleep. Usually when we go to sleep, we lie down, reduce external stimulation, and wait until sleep comes to us. The biofeedback-trained individual can deliberately self-regulate some activities (muscle contraction levels, respiration pattern, brain waves), which will shift the individual towards sleep.

Migraine Headaches Migraine headaches are vascular headaches. They are frequently one-sided. Biofeedback has been very effective with some migraine clients, but not with all. The treatment of choice (that is, the most common protocol for migraine headache) is skin temperature training. With temperature training of the hands, one increases blood flow to the periphery of the body and away from the brain, muscles, and spinal cord. The migraine headache begins with a constriction of the blood vessels serving the head, usually accompanying relaxation, followed by a sudden increase in blood flow to the brain. This usually happens as a result of stress or anticipation of stressful events.

What causes the pain? The pain receptors in the areas surrounding the cerebral blood vessels are stimulated by their sudden dilation. The brain itself does not experience pain; it does not have pain receptors. There are prodromal symptoms (flashing lights, light and sound sensitivity, etc.) that precede a migraine, with which the individual becomes familiar. They are slightly different for different individuals, but remain consistent for each individual. At the sign of prodromal symptoms, the individual can stop, do a relaxation procedure, and abort the headache. Sometimes the individual is able to learn an ongoing level of stress management, which means that the headache is less likely to occur. Once the migraine has begun it is very difficult to abort it.

Migraine headache sometimes includes muscle contraction precursors. In this case, you might begin with EMG frontalis feedback training or even some EMG training for the neck muscles and trapezius. Individuals who breathe with the upper chest, whose breathing contributes to headaches, can profit from training in diaphragmatic breathing. This training may include some EMG training to let them know when they are using accessory muscles.

Raynaud's Disease Biofeedback training is the treatment of choice for Raynaud's disease, a pathological vasomotor response which does not stem from another medical condition. If it is secondary to another medical condition, it is called Raynaud's phenomenon. With Raynaud's disease it is possible for the individual to learn temperature control. This teaches the person how to decrease the sympathetic outflow which causes constriction of the peripheral vessels. The sympathetic outflow can occur in response to environmental events, such as cold weather, touching a cold glass of water, or psychogenic experiences. The more the individual learns to increase skin temperature, the more he or she can decrease the frequency, severity and duration of the Raynaud's episode. EMG, EEG and other modalities may also be used for general relaxation training for the client. This is particularly true if the client seems to exhibit difficulties in achieving self-control of hand temperature.

Cardiac Arrhythmias Cardiac arrhythmias have been worked with using biofeedback. EMG, EEG and skin temperature (ST) have been used for generalized relaxation training and stress reduction as a part of cardiac rehabilitation programs. Feedback cardiography, usually done by individuals with special training and experience in electrocardiography, is a more specific approach to cardiac rehabilitation.

Tension Headaches (Muscle Contraction Headaches) Tension headaches or muscle contraction headaches have frequently been treated with biofeedback. These headaches, the result of excessive muscle tension, are treated with EMG feedback. The individual gets a reading on his habitual muscular tension level. Frontalis muscles, trapezius muscles or other neck muscles are monitored. This information is fed back to the client in microvolts (μVs). The client learns to reduce the μV reading, and to maintain an ongoing level of muscular contraction less likely to produce headaches. He or she can also reduce muscular contraction when feeling the onset of the kind of tension that usually precedes a headache.

PSYCHOTHERAPY ISSUES

There are two uses of biofeedback with psychotherapy. Looked at simply, one of those uses is biofeedback-assisted psychotherapy, and the other is psychotherapy-assisted biofeedback. In biofeedback-assisted psychotherapy, the client is monitored by the biofeedback instrument. The information from the instrument is used by the client and counselor as additional information (additional to the sensitivity of the good counselor). In psychotherapy-assisted biofeedback, psychotherapeutic information is used to facilitate the learning of the biofeedback skill. When the biofeedback instrument indicates a change in arousal of the client, he and the trainer may pause. When there is a change in arousal, it may be time to stop, explore the topic, and practice managing one's physiology in the face of the life event. The instruments used to augment the therapeutic process are EMG, ST, and EDR. EDR is the most commonly used because it is responsive to emotional changes that show sympathetic nervous system outflow. EMG can also be used, particularly with a frontalis placement, because it will give some reading of facial expression changes that are characteristic of the individual. For example, some people are skin responders (they tend to respond to stress by changes in the skin), and some are not.

Addictive Behaviors Alcoholism and other addictive behaviors have been worked with using biofeedback. Several biotherapeutic approaches have been found effective; several others have shown no effect. First of all, EMG, ST, EEG and EDR feedback have been used in general relaxation training. Some changes in self-image accompany the development of this control as part of the self-regulation aspect of biofeedback. This element of self-control seems to counteract the learned helplessness that frequently accompanies alcoholism. The individual who has tried and tried to control his or her drinking behavior and has been unable to do so gains self-control in another area of life through biofeedback training, and is frequently inspired to begin to exert control successfully with problematic behaviors. Group meetings as adjuncts to the biofeedback training are also helpful; group members can support one another and share experiences. The alcoholic usually has a limited repertoire of relaxation strategies. With biofeedback, this changes. Biofeedback training expands the tools available to the addictive personality for self-regulated relaxation.

Anxiety Disorders The anxiety response is a prime target for biofeedback training. Since we are all part of the "age of anxiety," most of us have suffered from varying degrees of chronic anxiety. A physiological arousal somewhat like fear, anxiety has no clear target. The physiological changes that accompany it include a sympathetic outflow, which increases norepinephrine and epinephrine in the circulatory system. For some individuals biofeedback training teaches a new way of being in the world which is free from ongoing anxiety reactions. This movement toward freedom is amazing, and may be accomplished in several ways. First, various biofeedback modalities are used to teach general relaxation training. The modalities may include EEG, EMG, skin temperature, and EDR. If EMG training is used to teach deep muscle relaxation which is then paired with events that usually produce anxiety, a new association can be formed. If you have ever stood up to talk to a group and discovered that it need not include a wave of painful anxiety, you do not know that this is possible. The task—speaking in front of a group—and the physiological preparation are two separate events. The physiological preparation is frequently an anxiety response. With deep muscle relaxation you can approach speaking to a group and complete the process before you develop the muscle tone necessary for an anxiety attack.

One of the ways of working with anxiety responses and biofeedback is systematic desensitization. Developed by Joseph Wolpe, systematic desensitization begins with teaching deep relaxation. The client is asked to develop a hierarchy of anxiety-producing events beginning with the least anxiety-producing events and leading up to the most anxiety-producing events. The client, relaxed, is asked to begin with the least anxiety-producing level of the hierarchy. He is asked to visualize the scene while remaining relaxed. When the individual is able to experience one level of the hierarchy without the arousal response—when he can remain relaxed as measured on the biofeedback equipment—then he is asked to move to the next highest level of the hierarchy. Step by step, he moves up the hierarchy until he reaches the target phobic experience. An anxiety response that concerns a distinct target is known as a phobia. It is great fun to work with a client, systematically combing through his or her life to desensitize the areas that have limited his or her freedom and flexibility. In a less systematic approach, the client can use EDR to monitor arousing experiences and spend some time during a session practicing managing his or her body in a different manner.

Obsessive-Compulsive Disorders Biofeedback has been used with obsessive-compulsive disorders. How is it used? By training the client for dominant alpha brain waves. One is less likely to obsess or behave compulsively while one is in the relaxed state that accompanies alpha. When he or she nears the target of obsession, the obsessive-compulsive client becomes more physiologically aroused. Biofeedback training can enable the client to decrease the physiological arousal.

Phobic Behavior Phobic behavior is a particularly good target for biofeedback. Phobic behavior is arousal related to a particular target, such as elevators, followed by avoidance of that target. The more we avoid the phobic target, the more the avoidance reinforces the phobic behavior. We are all mildly phobic about things with which we have had painful experiences in the past. We have learned fear responses to particular objects in our environment. We frequently do not have an opportunity to unlearn those responses. Biofeedback combined with systematic desensitization can be used to clear the emotional charge that we have about various persons, things, and events in our environment. How is this done? The individual is aided and encouraged to develop a hierarchy of experiences surrounding the object. The experiences in the hierarchy might include the name of the object, pictures of the object, visualizing the object, etc. In work with phobias, one may use EMG, ST, and EDR as adjuncts to systematic desensitization; EMG and ST to teach general relaxation training, and EDR to process the hierarchy. General relaxation training is followed then by associating the relaxation state with the items related to the phobia.

PHYSICAL THERAPY APPLICATIONS

Paralysis and Stroke Rehabilitation Biofeedback has been used with paralysis and stroke rehabilitation. EMG feedback is frequently used for muscle reeducation or muscle retraining. It is particularly useful for the individual who is experiencing very little perceivable muscle contraction. The individual is greatly aided by being able to see on the EMG monitor some evidence of the results of his or her efforts to innervate the muscle. If there is some increase in μV level, a phenomenon occurs that some have called "making a connect." The person begins to connect his or her efforts with actual changes in muscle activity. Initial small changes can be magnified with training so that more and more of the functional motor units can be recruited. It is tremendously exciting to the person trying to recover muscle function, because it gives him that very needed addition of hope.

Chronic Pain Biofeedback has been very useful with chronic pain clients, individuals suffering from a pain syndrome. EMG and ST have been used to teach the individual how to manage his or her musculature and general state of relaxation. When a person is tense, pain increases. It is potentiated by muscular contractions. EEG, specifically alpha feedback, has also been used to teach the individual a new relationship to his or her pain process.

Bell's Palsy Bell's palsy, a condition in which the facial nerve is compromised by a virus or other factor, usually shows recovery after six months or so. This process can be aided through biofeedback training. Biofeedback can teach the client how to equalize the muscle contraction level on both sides of the face through EMG training.

Muscle Spasms and Tic Behaviors Biofeedback has been used to treat muscle spasms and tics, giving the individual an awareness of the muscle that is receiving specific and inappropriate muscle innervation. This increased awareness of the spasming muscle enables the individual to relax it, to cease sending out the nerve impulses that temporarily contract the muscle or muscle group. This has been useful with facial tics, blepharospasm, and in some cases, Tourette's disorder. EMG training is the treatment of choice. There are two approaches: to begin with a more general relaxation protocol or to work directly with the symptom. In some cases, beginning directly with the symptom only aggravates the response. EMG is used to focus on the triggering mechanisms of the tic and to aid in training muscle relaxation and control. Tics, which are stereotyped behaviors, sometimes look voluntary, but are actually the innervation of the muscle or muscle groups on a reflex level. The use of a mirror so that the person can see the area as he or she experiences the internal sensations and the feedback corresponding to those sensations is sometimes helpful. Sometimes video feedback is used in conjunction with biofeedback.

Neuromuscular Re-education Neuromuscular re-education is the use of EMG feedback to let the client know what electrical activity the muscle is producing so it can be enhanced. It is typically done by physical therapists. The EMG electrodes are placed over the muscle in question, close together to make the EMG pickup as specific as possible to the target muscle. The sensitivity of the instrument is increased so that it is able to pick up the smallest signal. As the client is able to recruit more of the motor units, the sensitivity of the instrument is changed so that it will be more difficult to change the meter reading or graphic display of the computer monitor. This protocol was originated by Basmajian, who demonstrated with needle electrodes that a single motor unit could demonstrate learning. Surface EMG electrodes enable one to pick up the activity of a number of motor units; they are more suitable for muscle training in general.

Biofeedback has broad potential for postoperative rehabilitation, for example, EMG with back and neck injuries. Postoperative rehabilitation enables the individual to be comfortable following surgery. It may even facilitate the healing process.

The use of biofeedback with torticollis, which is so difficult to treat, shows biofeedback as one of the most promising modalities. Torticollis is very resistant to treatment using conventional means. In torticollis (also called wryneck), one or more neck muscles are spastic while the opposing muscle, the antagonist, is flaccid. This means that the head is chronically pulled over to one side. Spasmodic torticollis is a chronic condition that causes the individual considerable discomfort. There is frequently a psychological component to the condition. EMG training for torticollis teaches the individual to increase the innervation of the muscle that is not over-contracting. There may also be some benefit in teaching the spastic muscle to relax at some point.

Biofeedback has been used with chronic muscle contraction conditions. Some of these show up in postural deficiencies and poor muscle conditioning, and sometimes they are a result of chronic stress and psychological states, i.e., anxiety or depression.

EDUCATIONAL PROBLEMS AND GROWTH

Biofeedback can be used for educational problems. Since it can be helpful with many conditions, it can be used by everyone in the educational setting. This includes students, teachers, administrators, ancillary employees, and even parents. It can be used for educational purposes or for other services provided by schools. It can be provided by the teachers, special educators, school nurses, physical education specialists, or other designated members of the school community.

For educational purposes, it can be used to facilitate learning and memory or more directly for knowledge acquisition. Facilitation of learning and memory may take the form of helping reduce anxiety responses to school experiences: math anxiety, test anxiety, writer's block, public speaking phobias, and social interaction anxiety responses. It also includes more specific anxiety responses: phobias, such as school phobia in general, or more specific phobic responses such as to math in general or particular features of the school environment.

For knowledge acquisition, biofeedback can be used as a lab experience for data acquisition and processing—experiences with physiological responses studied in biology, experiences in psychological states studied in social science courses, etc. The school nurse can use biofeedback for medical complaints that might lend themselves to school interventions. In physical education it can be used to facilitate the mind/body integration exemplified by fine athletes. It can be used in a general way for concentration training.

It is said that children are right hemisphere dominant. A hemispheric shift (right to left) generally occurs between five to seven years (but not always). Sometimes in the case of faulty reading skills, the individual biases in the right hemisphere when asked to read; he then finds it difficult to comprehend or process the written verbal information easily. It is difficult because the nonverbal hemisphere has been asked to read; this hemisphere has very little language and definitely does not like to read. When some people become stressed, they tend to shift into the right hemisphere, which is the nonacademic hemisphere. Screening to determine basic neurological organization and learning styles might enable us to gear learning more toward the individual.

BUSINESS APPLICATIONS

Business applications mirror those of the educational setting. The stress components of the business setting are well known. These can be addressed by an on-site biofeedback consultant or individuals can be referred out. It is tragic to consider the individuals who are doing the best they can, but coping with physiological responses that complicate their efforts, as in the case of the individual struggling with chronic anxiety response patterns. This individual is frequently trying to appear as relaxed as possible while inhibiting outward signs of suffering.

SPORTS APPLICATIONS

Biofeedback applications in sports can be seen in the twin applications of stress reduction and skills acquisition. For each activity, the inverted-U of optimal performance is a graph of effectiveness versus level of arousal. Preparation for sports performance requires that athletes be aroused enough, but not too much. They need to achieve a balanced state of arousal for the particular activity. Biofeedback training, as it increases awareness, enables the athlete to notice his or her state of arousal. If it does not seem to be appropriate, the athlete can do things to better approximate the appropriate state. The adjunctive techniques for biofeedback for athletes include visual rehearsal, systematic desensitization as to particular aspects of the event, and so on.

In conclusion, biofeedback has multiple applications. It is indicated for a variety of conditions. It is up to the biofeedback practitioner and the client/patient to determine when it is indicated and what modality or combination of modalities and procedures is appropriate. Biofeedback focuses with clarity on the nature of the presenting complaint. The closer you can come to specificity in the treatment/training plan, the clearer the results. With this comes greater learning. Biofeedback instruction enables you to get a clear sense of progress and results, and this encourages you, giving you greater hope and motivation.

CHAPTER FIVE

CONTRAINDICATIONS FOR BIOFEEDBACK

"The therapist should be aware of potential problems arising in the course of biofeedback training as well as contraindications to biofeedback."

GEORGE D. FULLER-VON BOZZAY

"There is still pull a little bit on the neck but not enough to have long-range side effects. I am not doing them as often as I would like. On my winter break, I will make this a twice-a-day commitment. It is amazing how everything in the lower part of our body is connected to the neck and visa versa. I am realizing a new awareness of the seriousness of my injury. These movements are giving me a wonderful awareness of parts of my body that I have never sensed before."

HELEN ELAINE, BIOFEEDBACKER

Not everyone is a good candidate for biofeedback. It is important for the biofeedback clinician to know when biofeedback is not appropriate. The contraindications include psychophysiological "decompression" reactions; chemotherapeutic reactions; psychotic and borderline psychotic conditions; and familial or personal histories of epilepsy or incipient epilepsy (Fuller, 1977).

During the intake interview it is important to explain the benefits of biofeedback in general terms. Unfounded claims should be avoided; achievable goals, such as physiologic changes and symptomatic changes, emphasized. Physiologic changes include changes in the instrument readings, for example, a reduction of the microvolt readings on the EMG. Symptomatic changes refer to changes in the frequency, duration and intensity of the symptoms. These can be recorded in the client's symptom diary or log. Before the individual may notice symptomatic change, the biofeedback data can demonstrate change. Therefore, you can at least predict physiologic change. You also need to inform clients/patients of "anything that may affect their willingness to participate," or the contraindications. Not only do you need to communicate this information, but you need to communicate it in a way that does not represent a self-fulfilling prophecy.

Psychophysiological "decompression" reaction refers to the tendency of some clients/patients to decompensate when they begin to lower arousal levels or become more aware of their bodies' condition. Some individuals who come into the lab have psychophysiological adjustments that include a great deal of muscular tension; it would cause them a great deal of distress to begin to unravel the knot created by these adjustments. In some cases it is clear that in order to move toward increased comfort the individual would have to go through so much disintegration that it would not be worth it. In other cases, the individual is ready for that process and able to take the upheaval that it represents.

Chemotherapeutic reactions refer to the fact that as a person relaxes his or her physiology, there may be less need for medication. For example, less of the following medications might be necessary: thyroid medicine, insulin, and hypertension medication. As the person relaxes and the need for medication decreases, he or she needs to be monitored by the primary physician so that no inadvertent overdose of medication may be taken.

There is potential for using biofeedback to help epileptics manage the seizure response. In the ordinary clinical biofeedback lab, there is a concern that biofeedback may encourage seizure patterns, particularly through EEG training. In some cases, the lowering of the epileptic's arousal may put him or her within the seizure range. Therefore, it is considered inappropriate to do biofeedback training with epileptics unless the facilitator is trained in working with that disorder.

There is another set of contraindications that is constituted of psychological concerns. An example would be the individual with excessive secondary gain, such as the individual with litigation pending (secondary gain may be defined as an accidental benefit that comes from a presenting complaint, such as increased attention, time off from work, financial gain, and the like). Litigation tends to say to the individual, "Try to get well. In fact, we will be looking at the steps you have taken to achieve this, but don't succeed because you will lose your case or the settlement will be reduced." You can imagine how that might undermine the individual's motivation to get well.

Other secondary gains include the lifestyle changes that have occurred because of the illness, changes which the person is afraid to change. For example, a wife might be afraid to give up her ongoing headaches because she fears that her husband may leave her, or because she is afraid to do things that are waiting for her when she gets well, such as entertaining business associates. Or a person may have grown to enjoy the attention that his or her condition elicits and be afraid of losing it. The individual may even have developed a self-concept that includes the debilitating illness, and ceasing to be a person with that illness would mean loss of self.

The issue of secondary gain comes up in biotherapy after the initial enthusiasm. Sometime during or after the third session comes the end of the "honeymoon" period. The client may begin to be late or to miss appointments, to fail to do his home practice and in other ways to resist the training process. Such clients may be self-aware enough to articulate the problem, or it may be on such a low level of consciousness that they are not aware that they are bumping into secondary gain issues. If the secondary gain is too strong, the individual will not be able to benefit from biofeedback.

Another condition for which biofeedback training, particularly biofeedback-assisted relaxation, is contraindicated is endogenous depression. Situational depression, caused by environmental events, might be aided by exploration of the situation, problem solving, and biofeedback training. The person with endogenous depression, which may be the result of depleted neurotransmitters, may be at risk when the arousal level is lowered with biofeedback. Therefore, when a depressed person comes to you for biofeedback, the first task is to elevate the arousal level, if that is possible, before you teach relaxation. If biofeedback might be indicated for another condition, such as high blood pressure, this becomes more complicated.

The individual who exhibits superficial compliance is not a good candidate for biofeedback. Biofeedback encourages self-regulation and self-direction. If the client is complying with your requests, but avoiding actual experiencing of the process, then he or she is not experiencing biofeedback. This pattern is apparent in the way the client relates to the instrument's feedback and the instructions/directions that he or she receives, and how he or she relates to home practice assignments. As a practitioner, you will sometimes see it in the person who overdoes the practice assignment or who alters it in ways that defeat the purpose. It may become apparent that the response is too ingrained. Some other intervention would be more appropriate. On the face of it, biofeedback appears perfect for this person, but unfortunately he or she is not really open to the experience.

The recalcitrant person is not a good candidate for biofeedback, either. The recalcitrant person is very stubborn and refuses to comply with the suggestions. There are numerous reasons why the person might respond in this way. Perhaps he or she is struggling mightily to defend a fragile ego organization. Sometimes, it is a function of age. This is not necessarily a function of the aging process, since there are individuals of advanced age who remain flexible and open to new experiences. The recalcitrant person will not follow directions with regard to maximizing the biofeedback experience; he or she will not do home practice assignments, or keep a symptom log. After working with such a person for several weeks, it becomes apparent that the therapeutic alliance will not yield a truly cooperative spirit. It will be to the client's/patient's benefit not to continue biofeedback. Such clients/patients must be referred to some other intervention which may have a chance of providing the assistance they need. It is poignant to realize that biofeedback could be very helpful for the person's particular presenting complaint, but he or she will not take part in the experience.

In another category of persons not suited to biofeedback training is the unmotivated person. In some cases, the person is referred for biofeedback by someone else. That someone else might be an employer, a spouse, or a primary physician. In that case the motivation is that of the referral source. The employer says, "You learn to relax or you are fired." The husband says, "You learn to take care of the medical problem or our marriage is over." The physician says, "You have got to learn to relax so that you can lower your blood pressure level." The person does not have a personal motivation, but comes for biofeedback training at the demand of another person. In that case, the patient/client may have great difficulty following the suggestions of the biofeedback trainer. He will have difficulty doing the home practice assignments or keeping a log of symptoms. He will have great difficulty and even resistance in generalizing skills gained from the training situation into everyday life. In such a case, if the biofeedback trainer cannot help the person discover personal motivation for the training, then the trainer is better off referring the person to an intervention that will be more relevant.

Another category of client that does not make a good candidate for biofeedback is the person who is entering or terminating an intense personal relationship. This is a highly stressful experience, and therefore, people frequently choose to do biofeedback at such times. Indeed, biofeedback could be very helpful for them. The problem is that they are so intensely preoccupied with processing the experience that they can hardly hear or see the feedback signal. They frequently have an intense need to communicate their experience and their pain. This intense need to talk would be better served by seeing a non-biofeedback counselor so that maximum time could be devoted to the process of experiencing this upheaval.

Nevertheless, if such clients come to you for biofeedback, the first thing that needs to be done (if they are resistant to referral or are not already in a counseling relationship) is to process the interpersonal experiences until they are calm enough to be able to experience biofeedback or the other adjunctive techniques. In some cases, individuals have already begun biofeedback training before the event occurs. Their training may be disrupted for a period of time while they are in the acute phase of their experience. Then they may resume training, possibly on a more meaningful level.

Another category has to do with the individual who does not have sufficient ego strength to experience biofeedback training meaningfully. Even though biofeedback might be highly useful to him, due to health problems and whatnot, the individual with insufficient ego strength will have great difficulties in exerting the self-control necessary to make biofeedback effective. Such persons will not be able to do the home practice assignments; they will miss appointments; they will drop out of training without warning. It has been found in a number of labs that such individuals do not stay in treatment or training.

The individual who is unable to experience hope is another person who is not a good candidate for biofeedback. This is frequently a person who has developed a learned hopelessness syndrome. This individual finds it very difficult to entertain the possibility that biofeedback intervention will be helpful. He generally resists suggestions about home practice. He will often fail to recognize or acknowledge that any progress has taken place. Theoretically, if given enough successful experiences with the biofeedback equipment, the individual might be able to break through the learned helplessness syndrome. This is not usually the case in an outpatient setting. The individual frequently drops out of treatment after one or more sessions. It is unfortunate that even though biofeedback might be beneficial, he or she will be unable to utilize it.

In summary, it is very valuable to know who is a good candidate for biofeedback and who is not. Those who are not good candidates for biofeedback may become so at a later date. One would hope that they will learn the biofeedback skill so that it will give them relief from pain and increased well-being at a time when it will be maximally useful to them. But each person will have to make his or her own decision.

CHAPTER SIX

TRAINING AND INSTRUMENTATION

"The use of computers in biofeedback applications began before the term was coined, and has continued until the present time. A number of studies have been conducted with the aid of minicomputers or larger, mainframe computer systems. Much of the work in heart rate control has been computer-based, for example, and much of the work in the analysis and control of EEG activity has used computers, particularly in regard to the more complex multivariate analyses."

DAVID PASKEWITZ

"Biofeedback training has enabled me to become aware of myself as a whole being. It has given me the opportunity to be in control of my health and my body as much as possible. I owe much to biofeedback in that I have re-claimed my body. It has also given me the opportunity to be aware of my surroundings and how they affect me physiologically."

REBECCA ROQUINI, BIOFEEDBACKER

"Although skeptical at first, I believe I am at the doorstep of my body's potential. I am more aware of my systems and better able to meet stress. But most importantly, I have learned to relax and cope. Biofeedback has been wondrous!"

KEITH R. RORSCHED, BIOFEEDBACKER

This chapter and the four that follow it are devoted to a discussion of the standard (available in all biofeedback labs) biofeedback modalities. This will be an overview of basic principles. Books listed in the bibliography will go into the information in greater detail. Whether you are using or experiencing biofeedback instrumentation (as a practitioner or a client), this material is valuable for understanding physiological function. The standard modalities are skin temperature (ST), electromyograph (EMG), electrodermal activity (EDA) or electrodermal response (EDR), and electroencephalography (EEG). Heart rate and respiration measures are increasingly being utilized in biofeedback labs. Each section includes the physiological basis of the modality, the technological principles, and how it is used.

TRAINING SERIES

The following portrays a typical biofeedback series. The series begins with the intake interview. The second session is devoted to baseline recordings and goal setting. The third marks the beginning of the biofeedback training, which will continue through the termination session. In some cases, the training continues to criterion—until achievement of the desired level of activity. Whether or not the training goals have been met, they are discussed in the termination session.

The intake interview, part of the assessment process, is also used to establish goals for biofeedback training; what you might be able to get out of it; the outcomes you could naturally expect from biofeedback training; and possible negative experiences to be aware of. The client needs to be acquainted with everything that would affect his or her willingness to participate in the training experience; this is a contemporary ethical concern.

The intake interview covers the following themes: the history of the problem; the situation in which the person is living; the family history relating to the problem; the life changes that may be occurring at this time or at the time of the origin of the problem; other related problems; medical history; history of other treatments for the problem; the diagnosis (developed by the referring physician); and the prognosis. In a psychologically oriented biofeedback training series, life events will be more significant. In physical medicine settings, life events will be covered a little more lightly.

Toward the end of the training series, you will be apprised of the fact that termination is approaching, so that plans may be made for subsequent sessions and so the end is not such a surprise when it occurs. During the final interview, there is a discussion of the original goals and the degree to which the client has met those goals. This includes discussion of the training goals that have been met, such as criterion levels achieved on the instrumentation, and the symptomatic goals that have been met, such as a decrease in the number of headaches to an acceptable level. There is also a discussion of ongoing home practice assignments and how these will fit comfortably into the client's life.

The typical biofeedback training session might be divided into the following segments. The first 20 minutes is devoted to hooking up, processing the previous week, and looking ahead toward the future. The processing may be done with the EDR used to monitor the discussion. The discussion includes individual home practice experiences, difficulties with the practices, notice of progress, and decisions about how the practices might be done in the future. It also includes life events that the individual has handled in one way or another—successfully, using biofeedback-related strategies for effective handling of the event, or unsuccessfully, without using known skills or using them less effectively than he or she might have done. This, then, is an occasion to reminisce about past events and practice biofeedback until the client can keep the EDR quiet. When this is possible, the client can be said to have processed the experience—desensitized it, if you will.

Future events may be rehearsed with the EDR. The best possible outcome is visualized, and the client develops appropriate coping strategies using biofeedback skills. These future events are then evaluated in subsequent sessions to determine how well they were managed, how they turned out, and what might be done with similar experiences.

Dreams may be processed at this time, using the EDR to monitor physiological responses. The dream exploration is designed to help the client experience the content, interpret it, keep the physiology as quiet as possible, and notice which themes are reactive. The task then is to use those reactions to indicate themes that need to be looked at. Systematic desensitization or informal desensitization might be done regarding the themes. Certain themes can be used as suggestions for experiences that need to be added to the person's life.

Following the period of processing the previous week and upcoming week, comes the training portion of the session. The appropriate modality or modalities, as indicated by the general treatment/training plan and the immediate needs of the patient/client, are chosen. This training portion may include biofeedback alone, or it may be combined with one of the adjunctive procedures. The amount of time varies, depending on the effectiveness for the person. Training requires some rest periods and there is a maximum effective time for a given person at his or her level of development. There may be the need to use several modalities, depending on the goals. The training period may last for 20 minutes.

The remaining 10 minutes are devoted to unhooking the client from the biofeedback system and debriefing with the person about the experience. What were the internal experiences of the client? What strategies were used to achieve the results? Were there some unusual strategies that would bear repeating or including in the client's home practice repertoire? Were there some personal insights that emerged that should be noted? Based on first-person experience, can the client make any suggestions about how to make the training more effective in the future?

The training sessions follow this general format, with changes depending on events that happened during the week and new goals that may emerge during training. Forty-five to fifty minutes is a typical session length, but in some settings, such as in physical therapy treatment, a thirty-minute session might be appropriate. This is particularly true when the person may be coming for biofeedback more than once a day due to an inpatient situation.

After termination, follow-up may include a visit in three months to evaluate the degree to which the biofeedback skills have been maintained. There may also be a six-month follow-up and a twelve-month follow-up visit. In some cases, a lab may do a paper-and-pencil evaluation to determine the degree to which the learning continued beyond the training experience. Biofeedback lends itself to data gathering about its effectiveness, which makes every clinician a potential researcher.

BIOFEEDBACK AND COMPUTERS

Whereas biofeedback research used computers, clinical biofeedback was done originally with what has come to be called stand-alone instruments. In recent years, with the development of personal computers, biofeedback manufacturing companies have developed computerized systems (Figure 6.1). People like Tim Scully and Len Ochs pioneered the use of personal computers with the biofeedback process.

The computerized systems have some advantages over the stand-alones, and some disadvantages. The advantages include the relative precision of the measurements produced. The system can track the physiological changes and feed them back more closely linked to the physiological events.

They also have superior visual feedback display possibilities, such as a variety of colorful graphs—bar graphs, line graphs, histograms, designs (man-

FIGURE 6.1
Computerized biofeedback system
(Stephen E. Wall, Biofeedback Training and Research Institute).

dalas, geometric shapes), games, etc. (Enhanced audio feedback has also been developed.) This increases client interest in the process. The graphs provide a very dramatic illustration of how much value is being placed on the client's physiological events. I feel that seeing these graphs is very empowering to what might be called in self-psychology the grandiose self, a necessary part of us.

With the graphs one can see progress, shown in the changes that take place over time. The stand-alone instruments can tell the client where he is moment-to-moment. They can tell this relative to the client's baseline, which gives some sense of progress. The trainer can graph it for the client, and this will provide some general sense of the direction in which the client is moving relative to the goals that have been set, but this is not as clear as a graph that plots the changes during the session, as they occur. Looking at such graphs, however, does shift the client's focus of attention away from his or her internal state. This can be offset by deliberate attempts on the part of the trainer to keep the process personal and intimate.

The computerized system also allows the person to establish an intimate relationship with a computer. More than one of my clients have gone through changes in attitude from computer alienation, if not phobia, to acceptance, perhaps even purchasing a computer and using it professionally or privately.

Each biofeedback instrument is capable of giving quite a bit of information. Through tradition (in the field) and research, it has been determined what kind of information may be most usefully obtained from a given instrument. Therefore, it is useful to get an overview of what each instrument will give and how they compare.

Brain wave (EEG) feedback originally gave information about the frequency, amplitude, and percent time of the brain waves for at least one channel of information. This was often measured one hemisphere at a time. (It was considered that the human being was capable of perceiving and understanding only a limited amount of information at a time. There was also the notion that one can use input from only one modality at a time.) Today, however, people like Stephen E. Wall, Gary Schwartz, and others are challenging the notion of how much bio information the human can use profitably. For example, Wall records up to eight channels of information from different modalities measuring different physical systems and feeds back varying combinations of information. His goal is a more holistic shaping of systems.

DIFFERENT MODALITIES

In the following chapters, we will look at how each modality works psychophysiologically and technologically, and at its current application areas. It is important to remember that the information here reflects the way we currently believe the modalities work, and the customary application areas. These are subject to change with new clinical and laboratory research. We know now that our understanding of psychophysiological mechanisms is not complete and does not cover all of the dimensions. For example, our understanding of peripheral temperature mechanisms is undergoing change. The change comes from the recognition that there are receptors within the walls of the blood vessels that respond to hormonal differences in the blood. Constriction of the blood vessels is not just the result of sympathetic nervous system impulses. Nevertheless, we can use our current knowledge to guide us until further information enhances our knowledge and skill.

MULTIMODALITY FEEDBACK

Used separately, different modalities can be made part of a treatment/training protocol that is effective for a variety of presenting complaints. Multimodality feedback training blends various modalities for a patterned, comprehensive feedback system (Figure 6.2A, 6.2B). It was originally believed that we are not capable of processing so much information, but various people in the field of biofeedback have pioneered and demonstrated the feasibility and benefit of multimodality feedback.

The graphs throughout this book, beginning with page 8, come from the Biofeedback Training and Research Institute (BTRI), Cotati, California, and represent the work of Stephen E. Wall. The apparatus was a "custom-built computerized physiological monitoring and feedback instrument from BTRI and Mendocino Microcomputers." The eight physical channels were configured as follows: "Two channels temperature—thermistors placed right and left hands, ring fingers; two channels EMG (bandwidth 100–400 Hz, root mean square)—two-centimeter silver disks: channel 1, measuring the average of right and left anterior temporalis, and channel 2, measuring the average of right and left trapezius muscles; two channels EEG—two-centimeter silver disks: active sensors placed on 01 and 02, reference sensor placed on center of forehead; one channel EKG—two-centimeter silver disks placed on wrist to wrist; one channel BSR/GSR—two-centimeter silver disks on first and second fingers of right hand."

The graphs throughout the book were taken from two clients and represent two kinds: a 32-minute comprehensive evaluation pre-training baseline recording and 32-minute post-training baseline recording (Client C. C.), and longitudinal data over 21 sessions (Client A. A.). The comprehensive evaluation conditions include 5 minutes eyes closed; 5 minutes eyes open; 15 minutes talking about charged issues; and 7 minutes eyes closed, self-soothing activities. Subsequent sessions include eyes-open feedback with some talking.

In the mind/body training at BTRI, the goal is "achieving or reestablishing global homeostasis as reflected in the following psychophysiological levels:

"Hand temperature—a mean in the mid-90s with bilateral balance; EMG channel one—a mean of 1 to 3 μVs; EEG—reduction in mean beta/gamma activity; enhancement of mean alpha activity, exploration and enhancement of theta activity; EKG—a mean range of approximately 58–68 beats per minute; RSA—a sine wave pattern coherent with respiration; SCL—a mean range of .8 to 1.5 μmhos; GSR—minimization of phasic responses; respiration—diaphragmatic breathing and a mean breath rate of 8–12 breaths per minute."

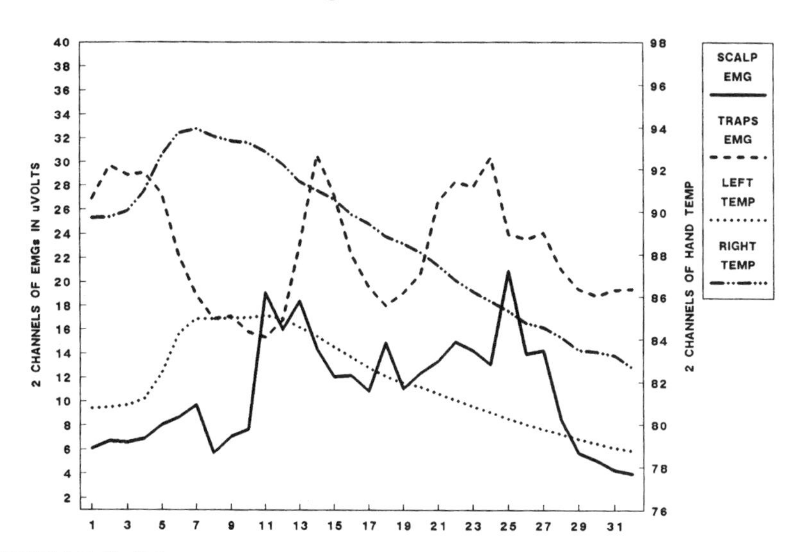

FIGURE 6.2A
Multimodality feedback showing scalp EMG, trapezius EMG and left/right skin temperature feedback (comprehensive evaluation, 32 minutes), Client C.C. Notice high baseline readings.

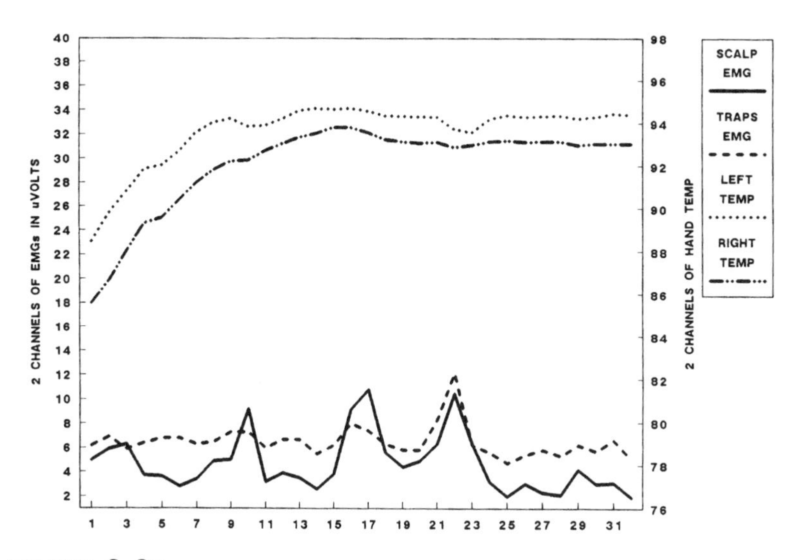

FIGURE 6.2B
Multimodality feedback, same client, same measures, session 24.

The following writeup illustrates the developmental changes that occurred during the course of client A.A.'s biofeedback training (originally published in *Somatics* magazine, courtesy of Stephen Wall). Client A.A.'s graphs can be found throughout the book.

WRITTEN INTAKE DATA

Medical Data

A.A. was a single, 46-year-old woman with five grown children who presented with tension and migraine headaches. She worked for the civil service, and had been referred to BTRI by a co-worker.

Her family medical history revealed that her father had died of a heart attack, her mother had irregular heartbeat and allergies, her sister suffered from agoraphobia, and one of her daughters had Addison's disease.

The client reported no drug use except one cup of coffee per day, and said that she had been hospitalized twice in her life: once for a hysterectomy, and once to have her varicose veins removed. During the past year, she had taken Fiornal, codeine, Cafergot and hormones. She also stated that she used feverfew as an herbal remedy for migraines. She reported that she no longer got colds or infections, although she used to get four or five colds a year.

When asked if she had any bodywork done during the past year, she listed acupuncture.

The client stated that she had undergone group psychotherapy and that she attended the Church of Religious Science, a metaphysical church. Her current health concerns included the migraines, which had begun seven months before, and the attendant symptoms of nausea and pulsating pain on the left side of the head that lasted for three days at a time. To combat these symptoms, she had used acupuncture, medication, and a jaw splint. She also described undergoing mild panic attacks in public places.

Lifestyle Data

The client stated that 75% of her life was scheduled and 25% was unscheduled, adding that this balance did not suit her and that she didn't "have time to do the things I want—to enjoy life." When asked if she could do one thing at a time and really focus her attention on it, she replied, "No, always worried about getting through one time—what's coming next." She stated that she could not leave her work at work, for she "always knew she had to go back."

When asked what she did to release tension from work, she said that she wore earphones and listened to "positive tapes" every day. When asked if that worked for her, and if not, how she might improve that, she replied, "A little—quit [her job]."

The client stated that it was important to have time by herself and that it was not easy for her to take what she needed because it made her feel guilty. When asked how her work added or detracted from her home life, she stated, "No energy, life—no fun—always thinking about going back [to work]."

In response to the question, "What is your most important relationship?" the client responded, "Boyfriend." She had been in this relationship for five years, and stated that it was changing—"I'm holding in my feelings more—don't feel like being physically intimate."

She stated that she lived with someone and that it was "sometimes" easy for her to express her feelings. She found it "easy to speak to close friends who are into growth and can express their feelings." When asked, "Is it easy for you to express your love?" she responded, "Depends on the person"; and in response to the question, "If not, what happens when you try?" she stated, "Will beat myself up mentally if I can't express it the way I want."

The client said that it was not easy for her to ask for help and that she felt scared and afraid of rejection when she tried. She saw herself as being more self-critical than self-accepting, and she said that it was not easy for her to know what she wanted and ask for it because she felt guilty thinking of herself. She stated that she was currently experiencing a great deal of emotional stress/problems in her life.

Hiking and walking on the beach were listed as hobbies the client enjoyed, but she replied "none" when asked how many hours she gave herself for these each week. In response to the question, "What new learnings or personal growth experiences have you undertaken in the past year?" she said, "I would like to quit my job and take courses to find out what I enjoy."

The client listed "buying material things" and "take a nap" as things she did to reward herself and "walking" as a thing she did for fun, but she did not respond to the question of how often she did either of these things. When asked to state three things under two dollars that made her feel good, she responded with "hiking, walking on beach, watching a sunset, backpacking, talking to a friend."

When asked, "Do you have any suggestions or expectations about how we might help you?" the client responded, "Learn what triggers my emotions—how I can control this—quiet my mind; also to be able to eliminate headaches."

TRAINING

When A.A. first contacted BTRI, she described her tension and migraine headaches, and indicated that much of her discomfort was work-related. The training modalities suggested by her complaints were temperature and EMG. Analysis of the longitudinal data provided during 54 sessions of training reveals some interesting information in terms of training effectiveness and patterns of arousal.

Since this client's presenting complaint was migraine/tension headaches, a traditional biofeedback practitioner might have trained her in one or two channels of temperature and EMG. At BTRI, she was trained in all of the channels and modalities. In A.A.'s case, this was fortunate, since the results of EMG training during the first ten sessions were mixed at best. Although readings at both sites were lower by the tenth session than they had originally been, they did not approach the goal zone and did not show any clear pattern of tension reduction.

However, viewed in the light of the following 46 sessions, these readings reveal a pattern that repeats at consistently lower levels. This pattern also shifts physiological location by appearing first in the scalp and jaw readings, then reappearing 20 weeks later in the right and left trapezius readings.

This switching of activity patterns between jaw and scalp and trapezius EMG activity was also revealed in the readings taken during individual sessions. These patterns indicate that the client has a particular psychophysiological mechanism that lasts for minutes and for weeks, possibly years. Over 56 sessions, the client learned to reduce system-wide activation to desirable levels, but not without experiencing repeating patterns of activation at progressively lower levels.

Conclusions about this client based on the traditional eight or twelve sessions of training would be startlingly different from those implied by advanced training. For example, the first 16 sessions of temperature training not only failed to increase hand temperature, they appeared to reflect a lessening of the relaxation response. Yet over the course of training, the client was able to achieve highly desirable levels of hand temperature and symmetry. In the same way, EMG activity decreased over the first ten sessions, but by no means as significantly as it did over the following 43 sessions. The fact that patterns of increasing and decreasing activity appeared first in one channel, then weeks later in another, suggests that such patterns serve to preserve an enduring personal strategy for survival that exists on a cellular level. Although these patterns are clearly ingrained and capable of switching locations, this case demonstrates that with sufficient training they can be changed, to the lasting benefit of the client.

DEVELOPMENTAL CHANGES

A.A.'s psychological condition showed changes corresponding to those exhibited in her psychophysiological systems over the training period. For a few months after leaving her job, she focused primarily on training, and included more pleasurable activities in her life such as visiting with friends and reconnecting with family. After approximately ten sessions of training, she reported reduction in the frequency and intensity of headaches, and by the 20th session, she reported being virtually headache-free. Her anxiety at being in public situations also gradually disappeared.

As she became more adept at psychophysiological self-regulation, she summoned the courage to attempt a number of pursuits, including joining a women's group, studying aikido, participating in a week-long self-exploration workshop, and taking courses at the community college (this in spite of her previous belief that she would never be able to function in a college setting). In addition, she enrolled in and completed massage school and began seeing clients.

In her interpersonal relationships, she became much less dependent on others for approval and redirected her investment of energy away from the men in her life and towards herself. She removed herself from a problematic living situation with a man and decided to live alone for the first time in her life.

This client began making more "right choices" in her life after learning that she was able to make significant and beneficial changes in her psychophysiological patterns, thereby freeing herself from the discomfort caused by chronic system overactivation. These choices were "right" in the sense that they were congruent with her intuitive self-knowledge, which emerged as chronic sympathetic outflow began to subside as a result of training.

Biofeedback systems (stand-alone or computerized) usually include sensors (some way of picking up the physiological signal, such as electrodes or thermistors), an amplification component (where the signal is multiplied by a factor called "gain"), a data analysis component, and a visual/audio feedback display component (stand-alones use speakers and meters or digital displays; computers use cathode ray tube monitors and speakers).

Preparation for biofeedback training typically includes preparation of the skin surface (often cleaning the surface of the skin with alcohol), preparing the electrodes (if necessary) with electrode gel or a similar conductant (some sensors are already prepared), attaching the active electrodes or sensors and ground electrode to the surface of the skin, plugging the electrode cable into the data acquisition unit or biofeedback device, and turning on the system, if it is not already turned on as directed by the biofeedback instrument manufacturer. (Please read equipment manual carefully and have appropriate training for its use.)

This chapter and the four that follow provide an overview of the standard biofeedback modalities and the principles for their use. The basic principles remain the same whether you are using/experiencing computerized or stand-alone biofeedback. The principles also remain the same whether you are using instrument-based or noninstrument-based interventions.

CHAPTER SEVEN

ELECTROENCEPHALOGRAPHIC BIOFEEDBACK

"The first of our studies on EEG alpha rhythm and consciousness was done in 1958 at the University of Chicago. William Dement had just introduced me to the techniques of EEG recording and dream detection in the sleep laboratory of Professor Nathaniel Kleitman, and there was much talk about dreaming, consciousness, and Stage I sleep. Because the waxing and waning alpha rhythm of the subject who had yet to fall asleep fascinated me (and perhaps partly because studying awake subjects was less demanding than studying all-night sleep subjects), I found myself gradually defecting from sleep and dream research. . . .

"Subsequently, in 1961 in our laboratory at the Langley Porter Neuropsychiatric Institute, we decided to train for alpha control directly, and devised the first of our audio feedback systems for this purpose (Kamiya, 1969). A tone in the subject's room was made to go on (or off) when the amplitude of the filtered, full-wave rectified and smoothed alpha rhythm reached a criterion threshold. When the amplitude fell below this level, the tone went off (or on)."

JOE KAMIYA

"Thank God for biofeedback! Biofeedback and many of its adjunct procedures have given me renewed strength, sense of power, and a refreshing spiritual awareness that I am still an active participant in the process of living. I still pray and meditate daily, but find myself doing biofeedback more and more each day."

HELEN ELAINE, BIOFEEDBACKER

Client was a 30-year-old male working on his doctorate in a nearby doctoral program. He presented with difficulty falling asleep. EEG recordings showed that he was 80% beta for both hemispheres. The electrodes were placed at the occipital placement. The instrument at that point was an Autogen 120. He received feedback to encourage alpha, some EMG and ST training to encourage the relaxation of his other body systems (also using Autogen instruments), and some cognitive retraining with regard to clearing his mind; adjunctive procedures/home practice included a meditation/relaxation process. After training, he reported that he was no longer having difficulty sleeping.

The word "electroencephalograph" (EEG) derives from "electro-" (dealing with the electrical or electrochemical nature of our brain), "encephalo" (brain), and "graph" (the plotting of the data). Electroencephalograph biofeedback is the use of graphed data to feed back information about brain wave activity so that you can self-regulate your brain waves.

HISTORY OF EEG FEEDBACK

A short history of electroencephalography begins with the discovery of the presence of electrical current in the brain by an English physician, Richard Caton, in 1875. In 1924 Hans Berger, a German neurologist/physician/ psychiatrist, used his ordinary radio equipment to amplify the brain's electrical activity so that he could record it on graph paper. He had a number of theories about how the EEG could be used to evaluate individual differences in ways that would be useful for psychiatry. He felt that EEG might provide some indications of personality differences. The story goes that he did not receive support from his professional colleagues. Indeed, he was laughed at and professionally ostracized. His writings on the subject do seem a bit disjointed as translated from German to English. Apparently, he committed suicide as a result of the distress he experienced. Probably, he had other problems, but his story is illustrative of the great difficulty an innovator has in getting his ideas across to others. Many of his ideas still hold promise for the field.

In 1963 Joe Kamiya, a social scientist at the University of Chicago, found that subjects given auditory binary feedback could increase and decrease both the amplitude and frequency of alpha. At perhaps the same time, in California, Barbara Brown was also investigating whether subjects could alter brain waves. She was using a visual feedback signal (lights of different colors). Later she heard about Kamiya's research. It was Brown who stimulated the founding of what was then called the Biofeedback Research Society. It was alpha feedback that captured the media's attention and brought the concept of biofeedback to the American public and then the world.

PHYSIOLOGY OF EEG

The physiological explanation for the EEG begins with the placement of electrodes on the scalp. At the tissue-electrode interface there is a transduction (transformation) of the biophysical ions into electrons. The electrons are attracted differentially toward the polarities of the instrument. Beneath the scalp through layers of the scalp, skull, meninges, and cerebrospinal fluid, are large groups of neurons (Figure 7.1). These neurons and their postsynaptic potentials are going through changes in electrical activity depending on the input from adjacent neurons. Neuronal input to a neuron creates changes which move its cell membrane toward depolarization or hyperpolarization. In the case of depolarization, each input moves it in the direction of firing and spreading its action potential down the axon toward the terminal buttons. This causes the neurotransmitter substance to be secreted into the synapse. The neurotransmitter substance impacts on the neuron with which it is interfacing. And so it goes. The electrical activity picked up from the scalp represents a vast number of bioelectrical changes occurring under the general territory over which the electrode is placed.

One neuron synapses on or touches the next neuron. The excitatory postsynaptic potential (EPSP) is a 15 millisecond depolarization of the cell membrane (usually a dendrite or soma [cell body] but sometimes an axon). These are excitatory synapses. This means that the input to the neuron contributes to its excitation. Numerous neurons contribute to the balance of excitatory or inhibitory influences. If the EPSP is sufficient to surpass the threshold of excitation, an action potential will be produced at the axon hillock. The action potential will spread the length of the neuron, resulting in the secretion of neurotransmitter substance at the terminal branches or buttons of the neuron to cross the synaptic gap and impact on the next neuron. The EPSP is the principal bioelectric event responsible for the electrical potential difference changes of the EEG.

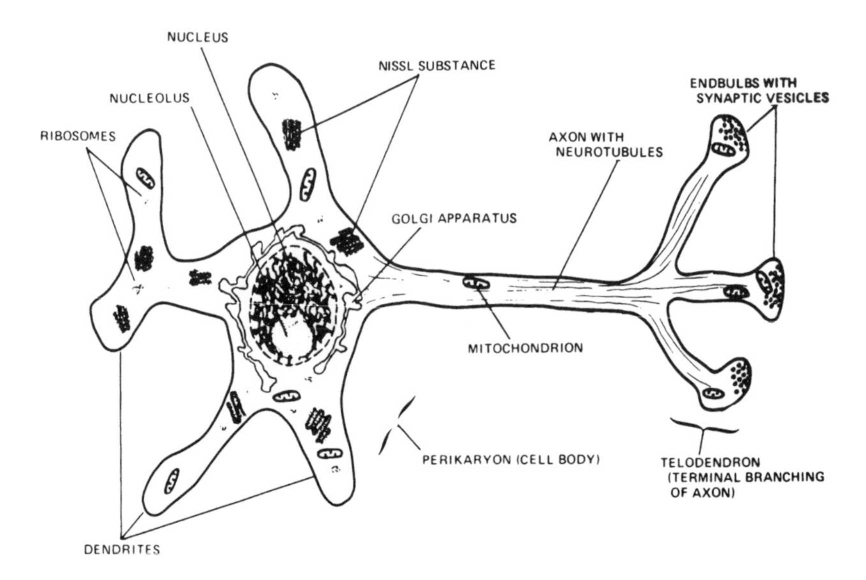

FIGURE 7.1
The neuron and its structure.

TECHNOLOGY OF EEG

Brain waves are represented by graphing the comparison of electrical potential difference between one location on the scalp and another location. There are two kinds of recordings: monopolar and bipolar. Monopolar recordings represent the comparison of one active electrode with a neutral electrode. The electrodes are placed relatively far apart. An example of this would be the scalp to earlobe placement, or scalp to mastoid process placement. Bipolar recordings compare two active electrodes with one another. These electrodes are usually placed rather close together—approximately 1½ inches apart. In clinical electroencephalography there are a number of patterns of electrode placement called montages.

An EEG montage is a pattern of electrode placement that has been developed in clinical EEG labs to measure the electrical potential differences between various electrode combinations. Using a variety of patterns, the EEG technician can find the abnormal brain wave patterns measured at different locations on the scalp. With abnormal patterns such as a spike, found in particular areas when looked at from different angles, and other neurological data, the electroencephalographer can assist the neurologist who makes a diagnosis. This then leads to a prescription and medical treatment.

In the biofeedback EEG lab, montages are also present. At this time in EEG research, the number of electrodes typically used is small. This is changing. We might say that there is a "phantom" montage with data being extracted from only one or two comparisons. The montages are designed to search the scalp systematically for abnormalities and therefore include sagittal placements, coronal placements, etc. Electrodes are routinely placed on the head according to the 10–20 system of electrode placement established by the International Federation of Electroencephalograph Societies (Figure 7.2). The 10–20 system measures the head from inion (posterior) to nasion (anterior), and then divides it according to percentages to indicate where the central row of electrodes will be placed. The head is then measured from ear to ear. This insures that regardless of the shape and size of the head, the electrodes will be placed in relatively the same place. It also assures that from recording to recording the electrodes will be placed in approximately the same place on each individual's head.

ELECTROENCEPHALOGRAPH

The electroencephalograph is a graphed comparison of the activity occurring at two places in the scalp. It represents the amount of electrical activity that can be picked up from the scalp. That electrical activity represents the bioelectrical changes beneath the scalp at the cortex level, which spread up through the various layers to reach the scalp. At the scalp the ionic changes are translated into electrons, which are part of the circuit that includes the EEG instrument. The signal is amplified until it falls within the range of our sensory capacity. It is in actuality the comparison between two locations on the scalp according to their electrical potential differences across time. This yields a graph or waveform. That waveform can be analyzed according to frequency (cycles-per-second or Hertz [Hz]) and amplitude (voltage, or height of the wave from peak to peak). In addition, some portable biofeedback units and computerized systems give a percent time reading. The percent time reading gives an idea of how much of a given waveform (the biofeedback trainer sets the parameters, i.e., 8–12 Hz, 0–50 μV) is present during a given period of time which depends on the time constant during which the instrument is

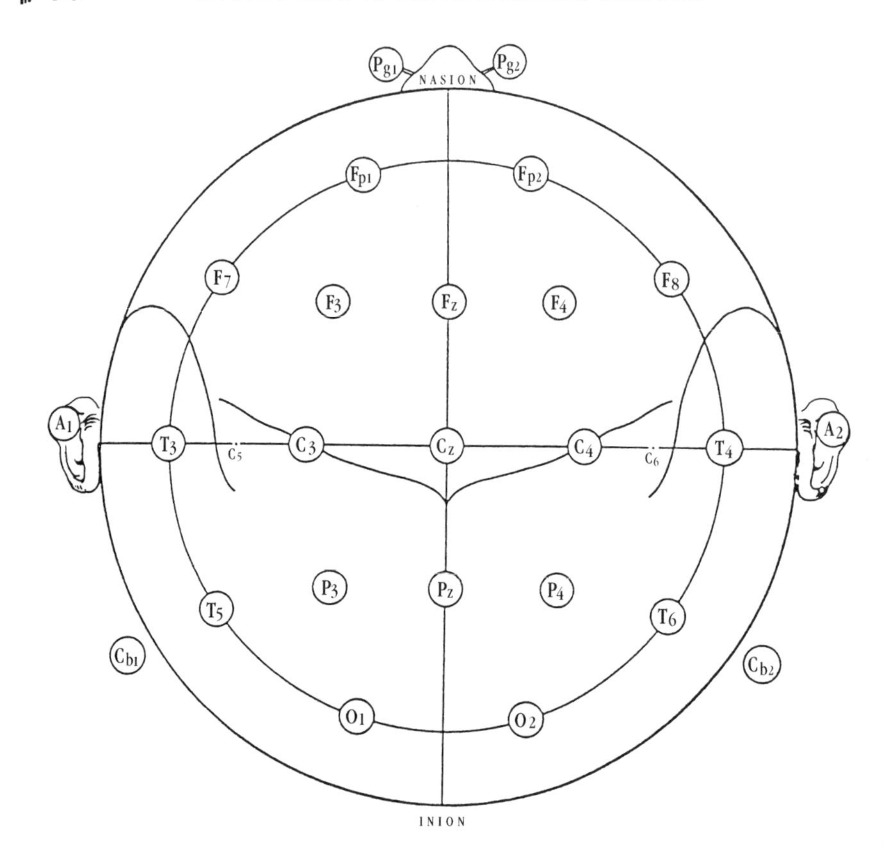

FIGURE 7.2
10-20 International Electrode Placement System. (after Jasper)

averaging the wave characteristics. Portable EEG feedback units do not display the waveforms, but usually have meters displaying frequency and amplitude. The unit may have a third meter displaying percent time.

BRAIN WAVES

Brain waves have been divided into frequency ranges according to the waveform characteristics and behaviors which correspond to them. These ranges are somewhat arbitrary, but are useful in communication among interested

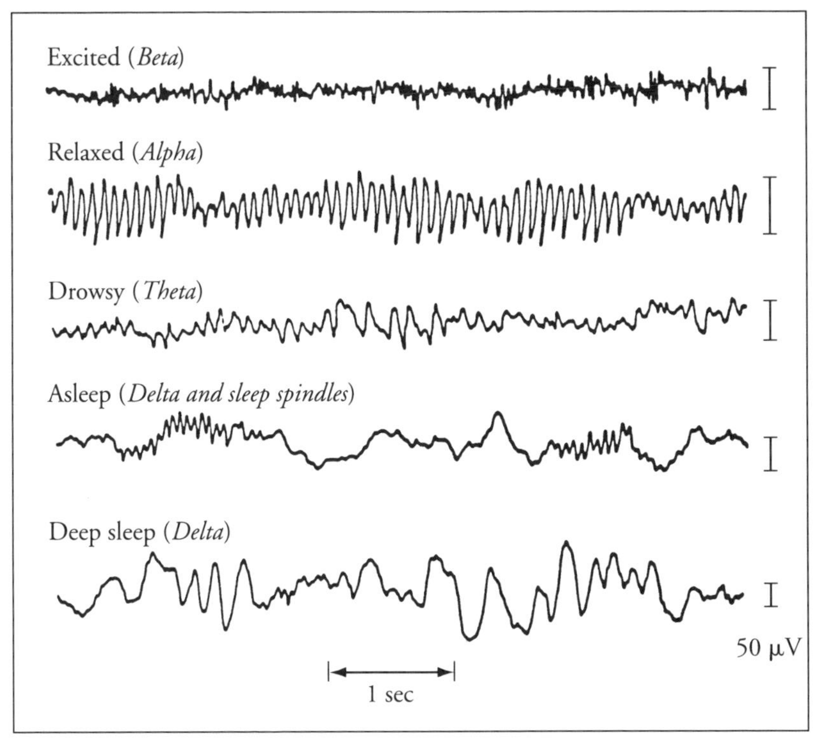

FIGURE 7.3
EEG frequencies. (after Jasper)

professionals and researchers. They have achieved usefulness over the years (Figures 7.3 through 7.6).

The first frequency to be differentiated was alpha, 8–12 Hz, at one time called the Berger rhythm because it was Hans Berger who first observed it. The other frequencies are delta (.5 -4 Hz); theta (4–7 Hz); and beta (12–30 Hz).

Alpha is associated with the resting brain state. (It has also been associated with meditation, but not all alpha is meditative and not all meditation is alpha. It depends on the internal experience of the meditator. Some meditations are quite internally active, and the brain waves correspond.)

Delta is associated with deep sleep. (This is differentiated from REM or rapid eye movement dream sleep.)

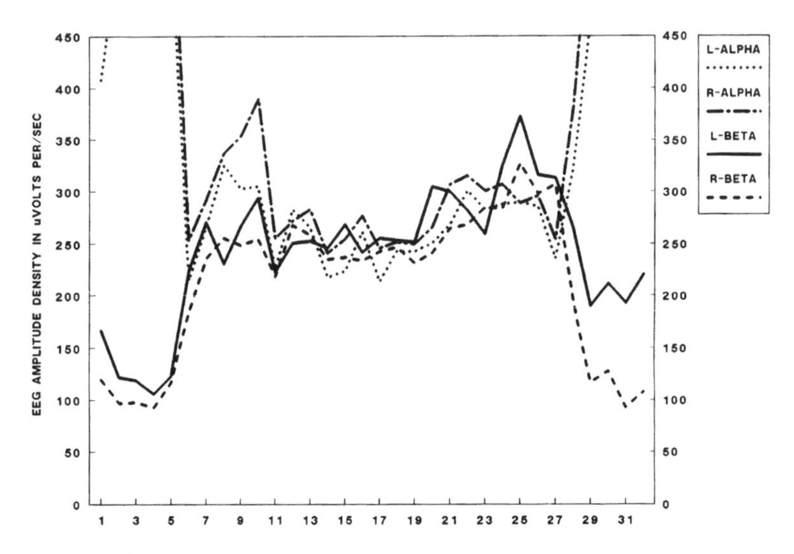

FIGURE 7.4A
EEG amplitude density during the 32-minute comprehensive evaluation session (right/left alpha and beta). (Amplitude density is defined as microvolts per second or frequency times amplitude.)

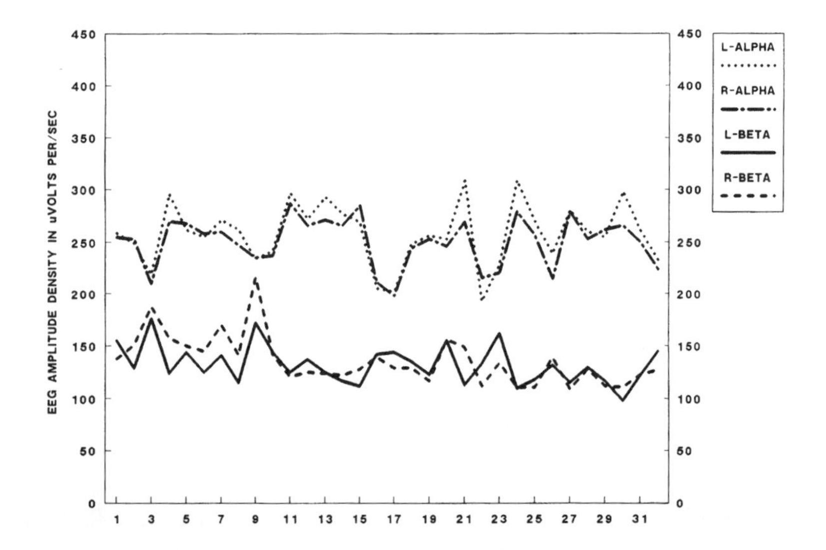

FIGURE 7.4B
EEG amplitude density during session 24. Eyes open mixed talking during session 24. Allow body measures to be calm and relaxed with a focus on EEG measures.

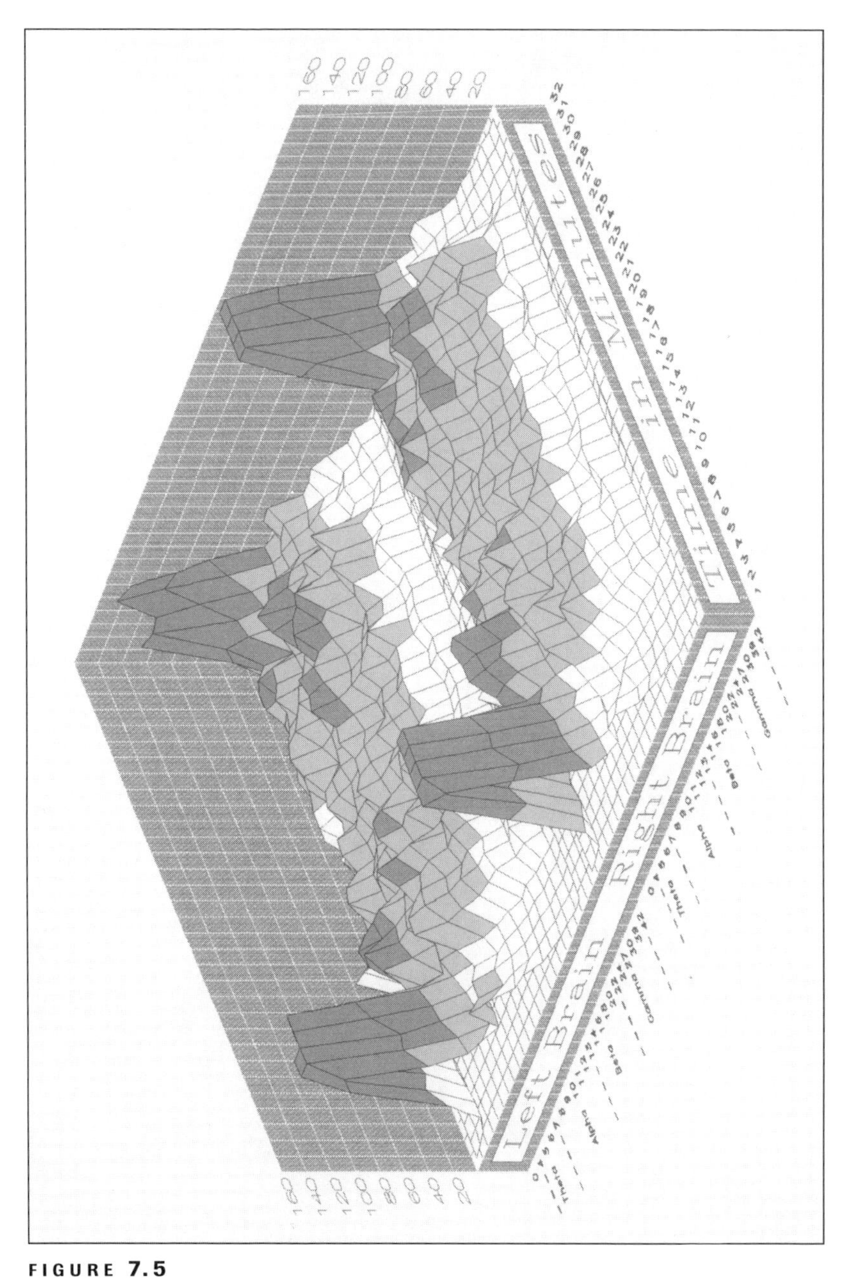

FIGURE 7.5

Topographical graph of the left and right EEG amplitude density during the initial 32-minute comprehensive evaluation session (Client C.C.).

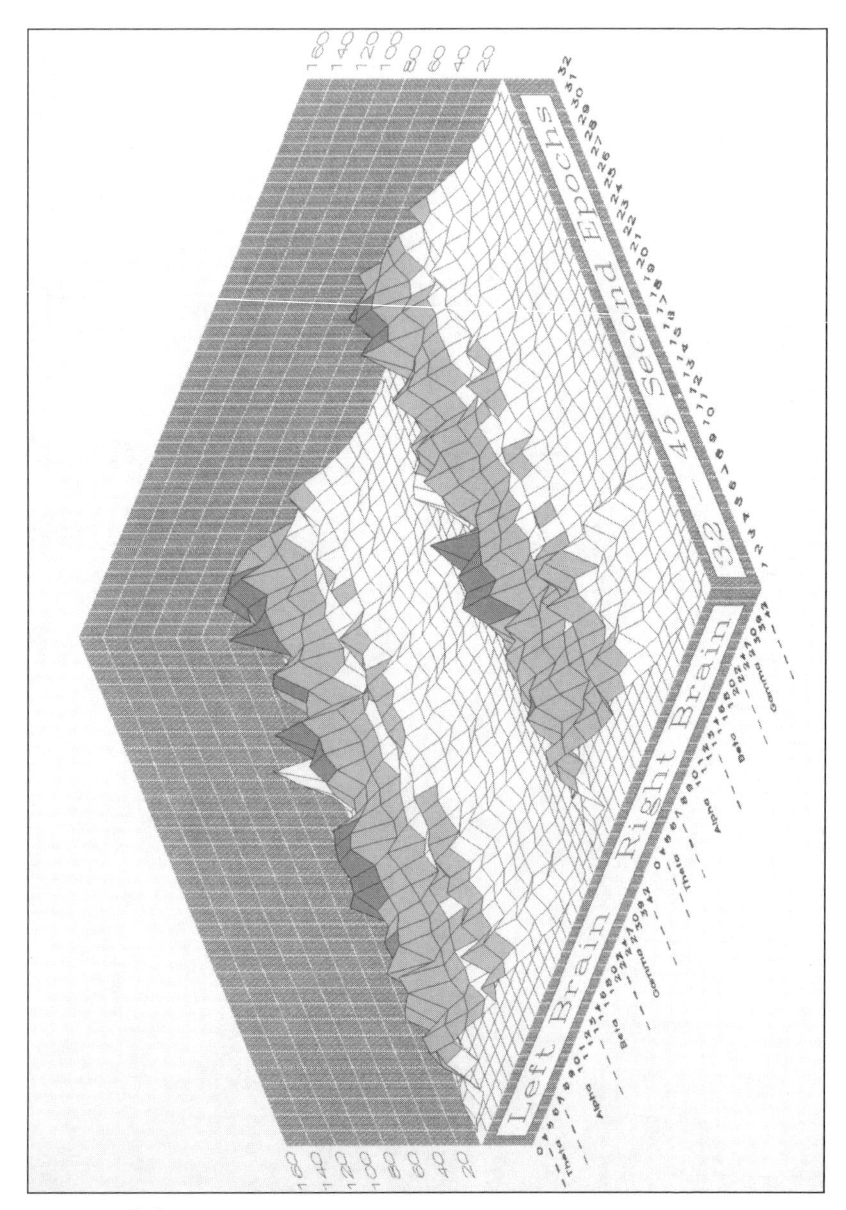

FIGURE 7.6
Topographical graph of the left and right EEG amplitude density, session 24 (Client C.C.).

Theta is associated with the period of time between waking and sleep which may be associated with hypnagogic or hypnopompic hallucinations. (It has also been associated with the moment of insight in problem solving, during which there is a theta burst—a short train of theta.)

Beta, 13–30 Hz, is the brain wave frequency that has been associated with the alert brain state. It is present when the person is attentive, excited, anxious, etc. In general, the hemisphere that is activated has more beta present, and the other hemisphere is usually in alpha. Research shows that the hemisphere that feels that it can do the best job takes over and inhibits the other one. The dominant hemisphere's estimation of the situation is not always correct, which leaves some persons in the wrong hemisphere for the task at hand. By and large we are able to bias in the appropriate hemisphere, but this ability is only indirectly enhanced by our schooling.

Looking at the locations on the scalp of the different frequencies, such as seen in a clinical EEG of 16 channels, we see that different frequencies occur simultaneously. One is more likely to find alpha at the back of the head in the occipital-parietal region. One is more likely to find delta in the frontal region. One is more likely to find theta over the temporal region. Finally, one is more likely to find beta in the central region. Biofeedback training usually records and gives feedback regarding what is happening in the occipital-parietal area as an index of the general state of arousal or relaxation of the person.

One of the significant aspects of brain waves is how they change over the lifespan of the individual. Brain waves from the delta range have been recorded from fetal brains. Delta, .5–4 Hz, is characteristic of the infant. The frequency increases as the individual gets older so that theta is present throughout childhood and alpha begins to develop in prepuberty. Brain wave frequency is somewhat associated with age (the association is inexact, but it can be used as a rule of thumb). In adolescence, the individual's brain waves are labile; on one day they are adult, the next day they are those of a child. This is very confusing to adolescents and to those who are working with them. It is not that the frequency speeds up, but as the neural circuits become interconnected through learning and experience, more groups of neurons are firing, storing potential and firing again at different rates. An analogy would be that with one's eyes closed one may see a fairly limited pattern, and the brain is increased in alpha. With eyes open, one may see a much more complex pattern no matter what is being looked at. This requires that the mosaic of the retina process the various interfaces and edges, colors, and black/white.

EEG FEEDBACK CONCEPTS

Electronics in EEG An understanding of electronics is essential for meaningful use of the biofeedback system. It is necessary to know so that one may understand how the system is working, and what may interfere with its working properly, from the physiology of the person to the instrument itself.

Most biofeedback instruments measure the changes in the bioelectric activity of a living organism. A byproduct of any physiological function is electrical charge. For example, ions are atoms that have lost or gained an electron. They are, therefore, positive or negative in charge—anions or cations, respectively. Of the three systems of information transmission within the human body—the immune system, the neural system, and the hormonal system—the one that has been obviously relevant historically is the neuronal or electrochemical system of the nervous system.

Differential Amplifier The differential amplifier in an EEG system is very important because of the vulnerability of the EEG to artifact. The differential amplifier compares the signal from two electrodes. When the same signal is picked up by two electrodes for any length of time, it is not a biological signal. A living organism does not produce the same electrical potential at two locations for any length of time. Therefore, what is being picked up are artifacts from some outside electrical source. The differential amplifier rejects the common mode signals.

Percent Time Analysis One of the ways that EEG waves are described has to do with the percentage of a given period of time or epoch that a particular frequency and amplitude combination is present. It is a useful general index of the brain wave pattern present. In EEG biofeedback the actual graph of the waveform is not presented, but some derivative of it such as percent time. Therefore, the goal may be to increase a desired frequency and amplitude, such as alpha, by attending to visual and auditory information about percent time.

Dominant Frequency Dominant frequency refers to the brain wave frequency that is present most of the time, that is, has the greatest percent time. It is a useful distinction as an indicator of general brain state. It is a rough index of degree of arousal. It refers to frequency, but it does not say what the quality of the experience associated with the frequency is. For example, dominant alpha may be meditation or simply the resting brain wave state.

Subdominant Frequency The subdominant frequencies are all frequencies produced that are not dominant.

Amplitude Brain waves, the result of graphed comparison of the electrical activity of two places on the scalp, can be characterized by frequency, cycles-per-second, and amplitude (the height of the wave). Amplitude is measured in microvolts, millionths of a volt. It is also referred to as power. It is proportional to the number of neurons firing at the same time. There are millions. Following their firing, they rest and prepare for the next stimulation toward firing. Peak amplitude is the height of the wave at its peak. It is one of the ways of deriving microvolt data in an EEG or EMG feedback unit. Peak-to-peak amplitude is one of several approaches to derive microvolt measures in an EEG or EMG signal.

Artifacts in EEG Artifacts that must be considered in EEG recordings include: electrode artifacts (broken electrode cables, corroded surface of the electrodes or scratched, unclean electrode surface increasing the impedance at the tissue-electrode interface, etc.); nonsymmetrical electrode placement (electrodes placed on different parts of the scalp); outside electrical interference (60 Hz interference, power sources nearby, radio frequency signals, etc.); defects in the apparatus (electronic malfunctioning with the instrument itself); movements (eye blinks, movements of parts of the body, EMG activity, etc.)—this shows itself in actual movement of the wires and also changes in brain activity based on the movements and activity of the somatic nervous system and sensorimotor cortex); and physiological artifacts caused by such things as food and drink, medication, etc., that are taken in and then affect the EEG in characteristic ways.

Behavioral Tests for EEG Behavioral tests that are used with the EEG to determine accuracy of the recording include having the individual close his or her eyes to see whether there is the expected increase in alpha frequency activity, or having the individual do mental arithmetic to see whether there is the expected increase in beta frequency activity.

HEMISPHERE SPECIALIZATION

Roger Sperry won the Nobel Prize for medicine for split brain research (he is the first and only psychologist to win the Nobel Prize). James Bogen, a neurosurgeon in the Los Angeles area, performed surgery on a number of epileptics whose epilepsy was severe and intractable enough that splitting the corpus callosum (which transfers information about experience from one hemisphere to another) to protect the healthy hemisphere seemed indicated.

We are aware that most of us are not "split brain" persons. There are persons who have been born without corpus callosums bridging the axonal fibers, but most of us have two functioning hemispheres that are joined by several commissures (bridges of neurons connecting the two sides of the brain), especially the corpus callosum.

We have learned that the brain hemispheres do not present as simple a picture as we entertained following early split-brain research. It is not as simple as one hemisphere specializing in a function without input from the other hemisphere. (A good source for hemisphere research is *Left Brain/Right Brain* by Springer and Deutch.)

That being said, we can take a look at the picture that emerged from the split-brain research as a way of analyzing the special approaches to input to the brain for particular effects. This breakdown of functions comes to us from work with stroke patients, head trauma patients, war survivors, split brain patients from the work of James Bogen (evaluated and tested by Roger Sperry), lateralized studies, positron emission tomography studies, and other research.

The left hemisphere is the verbal hemisphere for most people, even left-handed people. (A small percentage of left-handed people have their verbal areas on the right hemisphere.) Therefore, verbal behavior, internal or external, implicates the left hemisphere. So reading, writing, calculating, etc., are left-hemisphere functions. The left hemisphere engages in linear, sequential reasoning. It has a sense and appreciation of times and dates. It tends to be the more positive of the two hemispheres in its personality, attributes, etc.

Most of the adjunctive procedures used in biofeedback use words to relax the person, which involve the left hemisphere. Biofeedback itself may be activating the left hemisphere, if digital or verbal information is being presented. If the feedback is in the form of sound, light or graph, it involves more of the right hemisphere. The original instruction may be verbal, but requesting the person to picture a scene or feeling involves kinesthetic or sensory experience. The instrument may be hooked up to one side of the body, which suggests activity of that side and the opposite hemisphere.

The right hemisphere is involved with nonverbal information processing, such as recognition of faces, pictures and nonverbal symbols, music, and bodily sensations. Some people have associated it with the unconscious. One might say that the unconscious is not that far away from your conscious mind: it is right next door. When right hemisphere processing breaks through, it is surprising and may even seem as if it came from some alien source. The right is faster than the left in performing its functions.

As a rule, the hemisphere that feels it can do the job at hand takes over and inhibits the other hemisphere (Figures 7.7A, 7.7B). Most of the time, you select the appropriate hemisphere for the job, but occasionally the wrong hemisphere gets activated and you may have temporary difficulty engaging in the task. For example, if you are in a panic, you may bias in the right hemisphere, which means that you may not be able to speak very well or recognize previously learned verbal material such as an outline for a prepared speech or items on a test. As you relax in the situation you may begin to notice that you can recognize the material. A common experience for some people is to come in for a test, look at the items, and feel mild panic that they have never seen the material before. In fact, they may not have; that is, part of them may not have. The right hemisphere may not have seen the material before, did not study for the test, and cannot read at more than a minimal level.

The right hemisphere has been considered the intuitive hemisphere. It is in the "eternal now." It does not have much of a past, present or future. It functions best in the situation, problem solving with the objects at hand.

If you are trained in a field, you are more likely to be using both hemispheres in an integrated fashion. For example, trained musicians use both hemispheres in listening to music whereas nontrained music appreciators may activate the right hemisphere in processing music.

Women and some men tend to have a larger, thicker corpus callosum. They are, as a result, less lateralized, less biased in either hemisphere. The good news is that they have a variety of functions and styles available to them. The bad news is that because they are not as focused or specialized, it may take them longer to accomplish tasks. EEG biofeedback can help us understand our hemisphere activation patterns and help us develop new ones to access as yet undeveloped abilities.

APPLICATIONS OF EEG BIOFEEDBACK

The applications of EEG feedback include insomnia, obsessive-compulsive/ruminative depression, concentration/reading disorders, pain reduction, and epilepsy (Fuller, 1980). Alpha feedback can help teach the individual to shift brain wave activity in the direction of going to sleep. This is true even for sleep-onset insomnia and the insomnia that occurs later in the night. Rather

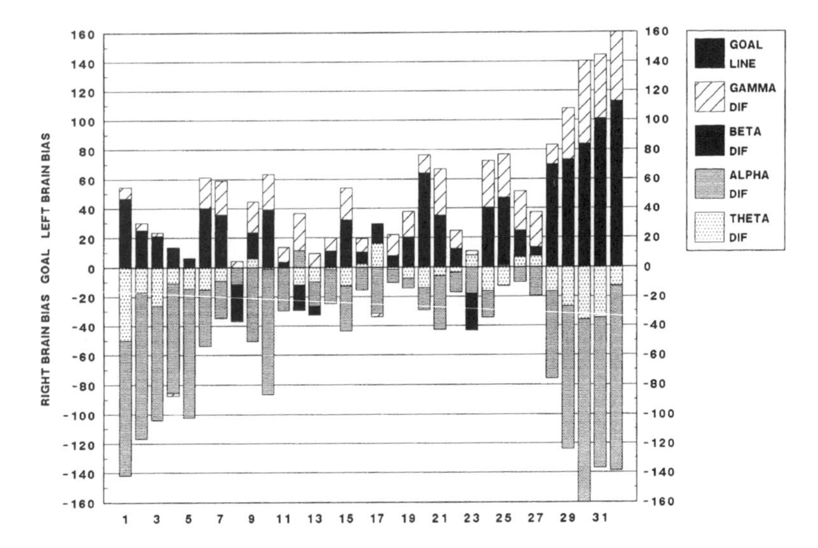

FIGURE 7.7A
Left and right hemisphere bias for EEG frequencies during initial 32-minute comprehensive evaluation session, Client C.C. (Theta, alpha, beta, gamma.)

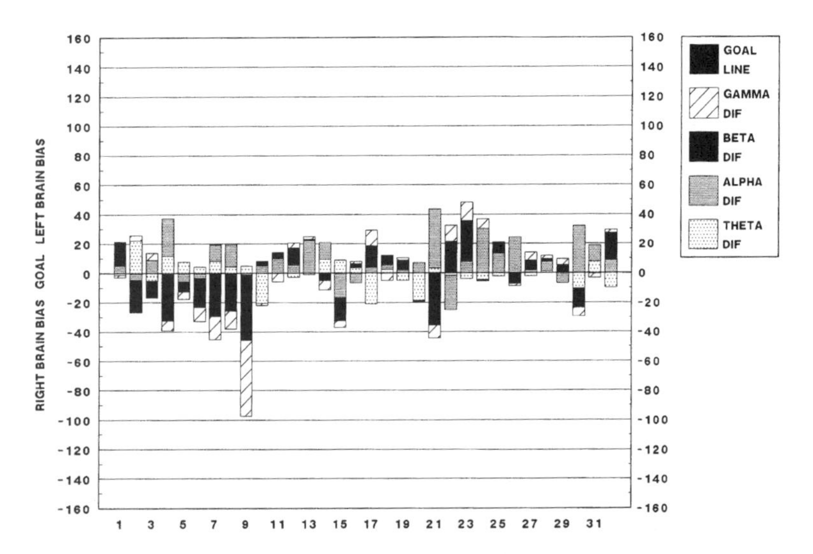

FIGURE 7.7B
Same as above for the same client during session 24 (note decreased differences: data are closer to the zero line).

than the individual waiting for brain waves to spontaneously shift in that direction, a deliberate step can be taken in the direction of sleep.

Alpha feedback with the obsessive-compulsive/ruminative experience can help mellow out the tendency to cycle the obsessive thoughts and compulsive behaviors. As one may notice oneself becoming more compulsive, such as checking the alarm clock a couple of times when one is more stressed, so too one will notice oneself not engaging in those compulsive behaviors when one is more relaxed.

Concentration and reading disorders can be aided by training to enhance beta during reading and concentration tasks. EEG training to encourage the appropriate hemisphere to activate during reading is also helpful.

Pain reduction can be aided by alpha feedback training. With alpha feedback training comes a slight dissociative state that is useful for pain reduction and pain management.

Work that has been done with EEG and epilepsy is classic by now. Encouraging the sensorimotor rhythm, 12–16 Hz seems to preclude seizure activity. M. B. Sterman's research with cats showed that they could learn to produce the 12–16 Hz frequency from the sensorimotor cortex. Along with this was the discovery that there was a decrease in seizure activity. The seizure activity had been produced as a byproduct of other research that Sterman was doing on the presence of chemicals in the environment of cats which caused brain damage. This was a classic example of serendipitous discovery fostered by preparation, knowledge, a keen observing eye and an analytical mind. From this work with cats, Sterman decided that humans might respond similarly. And they do. Persons with certain kinds of epilepsy respond favorably (decrease in frequency of seizures) when experiencing weekly biofeedback to increase 12–15 Hz activity.

Currently, there are two additional areas of application that are receiving considerable attention. One is EEG feedback with attention deficit disorder (ADD) children. This is also combined with EMG feedback, especially in the situation of ADD with hyperactivity. Joel Lubar and others have done considerable research and clinical work in this area. The second application area is EEG feedback (usually multiple channels) with addictive disorders. Steven Fahrion and others have been training practitioners to be able to work with this population and there have been some exciting results.

CHAPTER EIGHT

ELECTROMYOGRAPHIC FEEDBACK (EMG)

"The most dramatic application of biofeedback to large numbers of severely handicapped patients has been in the area of myoelectric biofeedback. Both for general relaxation, which alleviates many symptoms due to anxiety or excess muscular tension (e.g., tension headache, general anxiety, stress pain such as low-back pain, etc.), and for the treatment of neurological handicaps, myoelectric biofeedback has gained a solid following of clinical scientists."

JOHN V. BASMAJIAN

"I have come a long way over the past seven years in learning to relax and deal with stress. It has been a rewarding journey. When I was 29, I was told I would not live to see 40 if I did not get a handle on my stress. . . . I am happy to say that I have not had any of these symptoms for seven years and with biofeedback and stress management, I hope I never will again. I am so thankful for all that I am learning about caring for my holistic self."

HELEN ELAINE, BIOFEEDBACKER

Electromyographic feedback is concerned with measuring the electrical activity of the muscles. The electromyograph is similar to the EEG, but is concerned with a higher frequency range. There is a point of overlap between the two ranges. This means that sometimes EMG activity can be picked up in the EEG. For example, scalp muscle activity can sometimes be read as beta or gamma.

A 50-year-old male was referred to the Novato Institute to work with muscle contraction headaches. He was in a very stressful job in the human services which required him to be alert all the time due to unexpected changes in the activities of his clients. This job also required that he lift heavy, difficult-to-handle loads when needed. There were many and varied activities in this job. He lived alone and had many interests. We did a baseline recording and a series of eight EMG feedback training sessions. He responded quickly and was soon able to do his home practice, in which he chose to do Benson's "one" and passive progressive relaxation. He was very self-disciplined. He soon reported that he was headache free.

EMG biofeedback involves a comparison of two electrodes placed on the skin over the belly of the muscle. There is an analysis of the data, which can be read as frequency and amplitude. The typical practice among EMG biofeedback equipment manufacturers is to focus on the amplitude of the signal, the height of the wave. This is read in microvolts (μV). It is found to be directly proportional to the number of motor units firing at one time. As the amplitude increases, the number of motor units activated increases. EMG feedback training aims toward decreasing or increasing μV levels, depending on the purpose of the training (Figures 8.1A, 8.1B).

HISTORY OF EMG FEEDBACK

The history of EMG begins with the work of John Basmajian (1963), in which he discovered that the single motor unit could learn. He used needle electrodes and feedback. The feedback signal was displayed on an oscilloscope and a loudspeaker. (An oscilloscope is a cathode ray tube across which a stream of electrons sweep. It records moment-by-moment fluctuations of a signal by means of alterations of the surface by an electron beam.) The subjects learning to control the firing rates of different motor units within the muscle could vary the rate and even produce various rhythms.

In 1969, Thomas Budzynski and Johann Stoyva began their research with EMG feedback for whole muscle groups. Their subjects received auditory

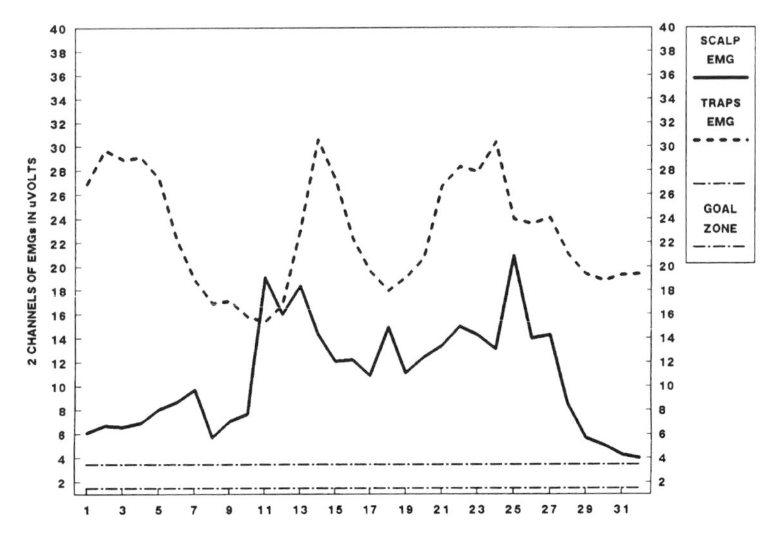

FIGURE 8.1A
Scalp EMG and trapezius EMG measures in microvolts during the 32-minute comprehensive evaluation, Client C.C.

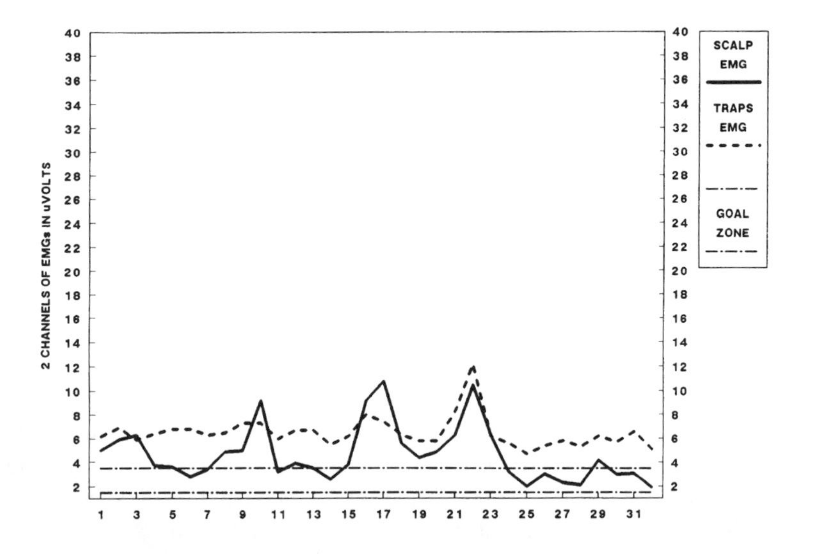

FIGURE 8.1B
Scalp and trapezius EMG measures taken during session 24.

feedback for frontalis muscle tension. They were able to lower their microvolt levels significantly after three twenty-minute training sessions.

There is an advantage in biofeedback in the use of surface electrodes. Surface electrodes do not pick up discrete changes in separate motor units; they are a more gross indication of muscle activity. The activity of large numbers of motor units are reflected in the electrical potential difference changes. This is advantageous because in EMG biofeedback one is usually interested in the holistic activity of the muscle—its general contraction levels.

PHYSIOLOGICAL MECHANISMS OF EMG (PERIPHERAL)

The physiological mechanisms of EMG concern the activity of the motor units located under or near the electrodes. The electrodes are placed on the surface of the skin over the "belly" of the muscle. At that location numerous motor units synapse on the motor end plates located on the surface of the muscle fibers.

The structure of a muscle includes muscle fibers and connective tissue. The connective tissue binds the muscle fibers together. How many muscle fibers and what their size is depends on the location of the muscle and its role in movement, as well as its representation on the motor homunculus in the brain. Large muscles, involved in gross motor movements, have a smaller representation on the motor homunculus (Figure 8.2A). Smaller muscles, involved in fine motor movements, have a greater representation on the motor homunculus.

Muscle fibers are very thin, approximately 0.1 mm wide. They vary in length to up to 310 mm (Basmajian, 1974). The function of the fibers of a muscle is contraction. Stimulation of the muscle fibers by their neuron causes contraction. The contraction may result in shortening the muscle fiber up to 57 percent of its length at rest. When a muscle contracts, the muscle fibers alternate: some contract while others, part of other motor units, do not contract. This enables the muscle to achieve contraction and maintain it as different muscle fiber groups contract and then prepare to contract again.

The motor unit includes the neuron and the muscle fibers upon which it synapses (Figure 8.3). A motor unit is a functional unit. When the neuron, which has its cell body located in the spinal cord, receives enough input from other neurons that synapse on it, its cell membrane will shift its polarization to a level past the threshold of excitation, and the neuron will fire. With the firing comes an action potential that is conducted down the axon to the

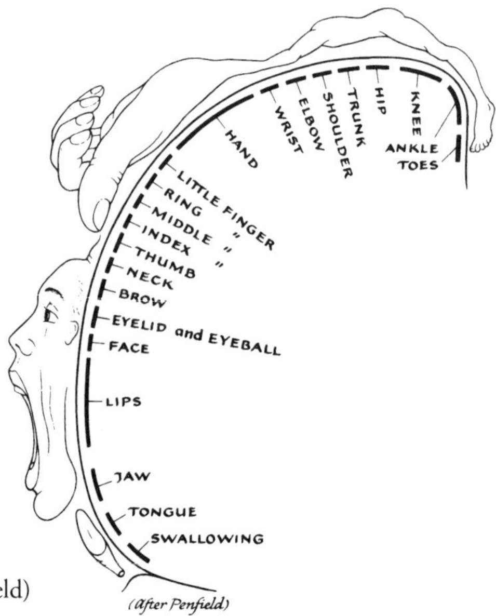

FIGURE 8.2A
Motor homunculus. (after Penfield)

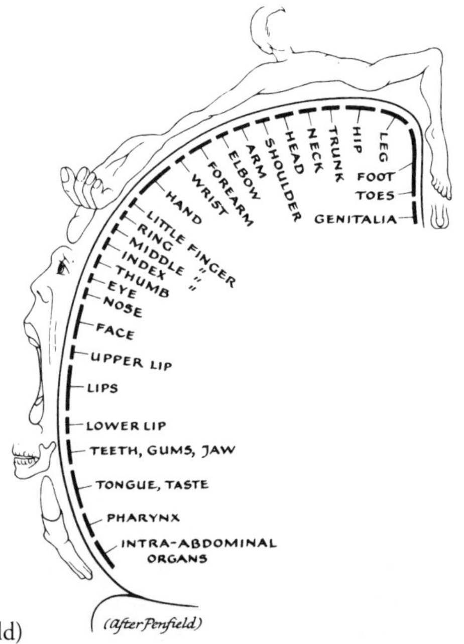

FIGURE 8.2B
Sensory homunculus. (after Penfield)

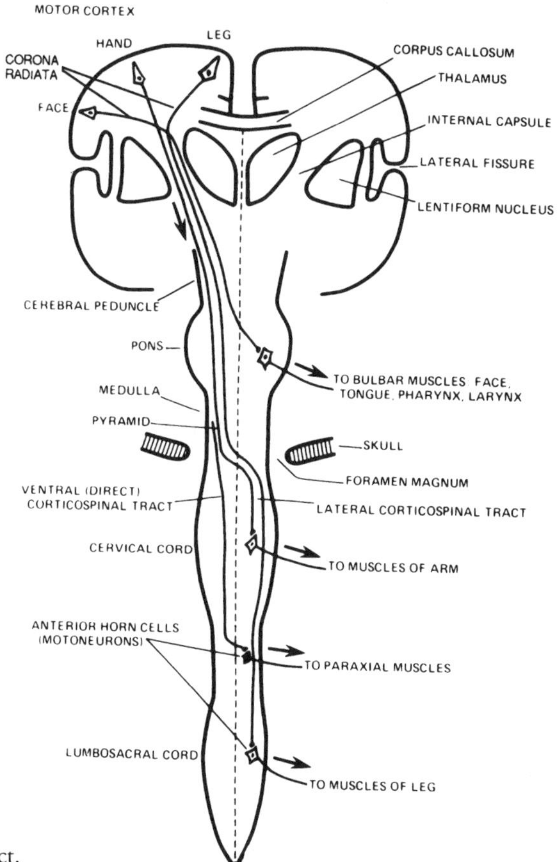

FIGURE 8.2C
The pyramidal tract.

terminal branches, where (given enough strength of the action potential) transmitter substance will be secreted at the synapse. The transmitter substance is acetylcholine. It bridges the gap, is received by the receptor sites on the post-synaptic membrane, and the contraction of muscle fibers is begun.

After a motor unit has completed its process, it no longer contributes to muscle contraction. Adjacent neurons are recruited to continue the overall contraction of the muscle.

Muscles can do only one thing: contract. The pattern of contraction and subsequent relaxation or noncontraction of muscles enables one to move one's arms and legs in various positions. The muscles that are currently contracting

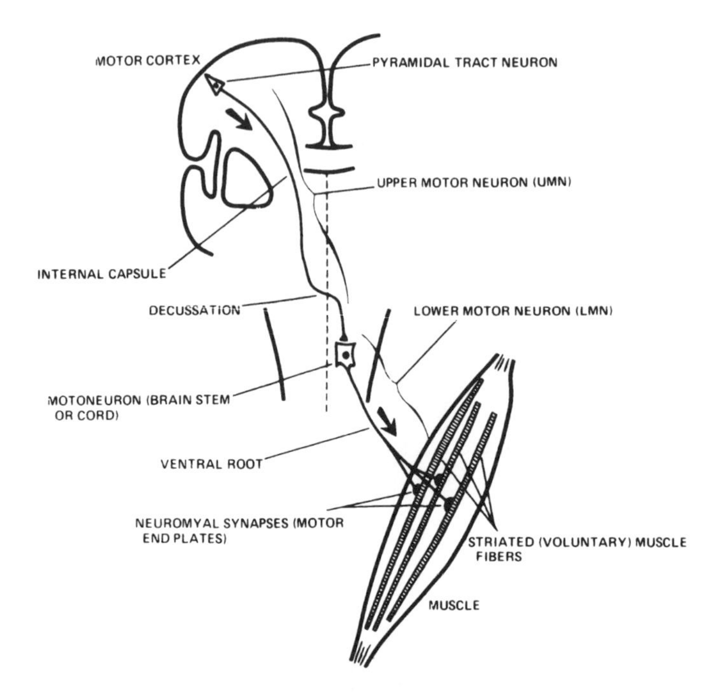

FIGURE 8.3
Upper motor neuron from the cortex to the brainstem or spinal cord; lower motor neuron from the spinal segment to the muscle. The motor unit includes the lower motor neuron and its muscle fibers.

are called agonists; the opposing muscles are antagonists. Muscles take turns serving as agonists and antagonists. What role they play depends on whether the limbs are being pulled toward or away from the body.

The unchanging roles that muscles play are those of extensor and flexer. Some muscles are called flexers because they tend to move the limbs, etc., toward the midline or center of the body. Others are called extensors because they move the limbs away from the midline of the body.

CENTRAL MECHANISMS OF EMG BIOFEEDBACK

The voluntary control of motor unit firing is initiated by the voluntary motor cortex (Figure 8.2A). The sensory cortex is also involved (see Figure 8.2B).

The impetus to move does not originate with the voluntary motor cortex, but with the association cortex, limbic system, and other areas. The voluntary motor cortex helps carry out the motor plan developed by other areas. It has many more inhibitory neurons than excitatory neurons. Therefore, the voluntary motor cortex is particularly involved in inhibiting, at the spinal cord level, unwanted muscle contractions; this allows us to contract the appropriate muscles to carry out a movement (Figure 8.2C). The decrease in μV level during in EMG training represents a decrease in the number of motor units that are firing and, therefore, a decrease in muscle contraction. Your brain creates the changes by inhibiting or decreasing the number of motor units by way of its "upper motor neuron." The voluntary motor cortex decreases the somatic nervous system outflow by way of central brain mechanisms.

It has been considered that EMG training creates some central changes, particularly in the case of stroke rehabilitation, which include recruiting neurons that are still functional, fostering the use of redundant neuronal pathways, and perhaps developing new neuronal pathways, which might include changes in dendrite growth.

TECHNOLOGY OF EMG

At the midpoint of the muscle, the belly of the muscle, all of the neurons connect to or synapse on the muscle fibers at the motor end plates. This is why the EMG electrode is placed over the belly of the muscle in EMG feedback training. EMG electrodes are placed along the direction of the muscle fibers at the surface of the skin above the muscle. The microvoltage of the EMG is directly proportional to the muscle contraction. The muscle contraction level determines the degree of muscle relaxation and tonus. The EMG detects the electrical muscle action potential (MAP). This is produced as the muscle contracts.

When change occurs in the electrical potential along the fiber, it is picked up and amplified so that it can communicate a signal within our sensory range. The amplification occurs with a multiplication of voltage of the wave by a factor called gain. This is then displayed in the form of a sound, light, digital information, etc. Surface electrodes are very effective in measuring the activity of the whole muscle or muscle group. Surrounding muscles are also sometimes measured artifactually, which is at times beneficial because it encourages the individual to generalize the relaxation rather than keep it restricted to one area.

The microvolt reading is directly proportional to the intensity of the amplitude of the waveform. The waveform is created through the comparison of the electrical potential difference between the two active electrodes usually placed some distance apart over the belly of the muscle.

It is very valuable to know the muscles of the body and how to palpate the appropriate locations for electrode placement.

BEHAVIORAL TESTS FOR EMG

Once the electrodes have been attached over the muscle and the instrument is turned on long enough to stabilize, a behavioral test needs to be conducted to make sure the changes in instrument readings correspond to the change in muscle contraction. The behavioral test used depends on the muscle being monitored. For example, shrugging or lifting the shoulders is appropriate for an upper trapezius electrode placement recording, and so forth.

EMG ARTIFACTS

EMG artifacts include 60 Hz, EKG (electrocardiogram) and EDA (electrodermal activity when measured). The main source of artifacts for the EMG centers around the 60 Hz frequency that sometimes affects the EMG signals (see also artifacts from EEG). The 60 Hz frequency originates with the frequency being put out by electrical lighting sources such as fluorescent lights. The EMG is vulnerable to this artifact because the range of frequency of interest in the EMG recording includes the 60 Hz frequency information.

Wherever there is the same activity being recorded at two sites for any length of time, it stems from a nonorganic electrical source. A live organism has many electrochemical events going on all the time, and the sites vary when compared with one another. Therefore, when the same signal is being picked up by two sites for an extended period, the source is nonorganic.

The EMG can pick up the ambient (room or environment) electrical signal or electromagnetic interference (EMI) at several locations in the biofeedback system. It can pick it up at the instrument level with faulty input jack connections. It can pick it up at a broken electrode cable site.

EKG artifact refers to the pickup of heart electrical activity by the EMG instrument. The EKG can be seen in the instrument reaction when the electrodes are placed in an area close enough to the heart. Therefore, electrodes placed on the trapezius muscles or over the upper or lower back (and sometimes neck) muscles will show EKG signals. This EKG artifact can be recognized by the very regular elevations of μV readings. If an oscilloscope or chart recording is reflecting raw (unfiltered) EMG, the characteristic EKG waveform will be visible.

The way to minimize the EKG artifact is to move the electrodes to a more distant site, if possible. One may change the bandwidth of the EMG, or use filters designed to filter out EKG signals. (If the instrument has these filters, one will not see EKG signals in recordings even though the electrodes are placed in spots that would normally show them). If EKG signals cannot be avoided, clients may be instructed to ignore them and concentrate on the more characteristic EMG signal or baseline signal. The computer can be set to "smooth" the graph to decrease the EKG artifact.

APPLICATIONS OF EMG

The EMG is used in most biofeedback training laboratories. It is used for a variety of presenting complaints, including the following, which have had enough clinical and laboratory support to be considered standard applications of EMG training: general relaxation training, phobic desensitization/anxiety reduction, tension (muscle contraction) headaches, neck and back pain, essential hypertension, bruxism/temporomandibular joint syndrome, neuromuscular re-education/stroke, and cerebral palsy (Fuller, 1980).

With general relaxation training the frontalis electrode placement may be used, or if the individual seems to hold more tension in a particular muscle group, the electrodes may be placed along the upper trapezius, for example. When general relaxation has been achieved, then it will be possible to move on to more specific work with the individual's presenting problem. Phobic desensitization/anxiety reduction begins with general relaxation training and then moves on toward pairing the relaxation response with the target of the phobia and its impact. Anxiety reduction also begins with general relaxation training using the EMG and then moves on toward relating that relaxation response to life experiences. Essential hypertension using a frontalis and other placements teaches the person how to maintain a relaxed musculature and when to relax it when it becomes more tense. Bruxism/temporomandibular joint syndrome uses a masseter placement and teaches the individual to lower the tension level of the masseter at rest and then during life experiences. Neuromuscular re-education/stroke generally focuses on the muscles or muscle groups where there is muscle weakness and provides feedback so the individual can increase muscle tonus. Cerebral palsy uses EMG feedback to reduce spasticity of the muscle or muscle groups in question.

EMG biofeedback is used to teach general relaxation. Relaxing the musculature is a big step toward relaxation of other body systems. Relaxing the musculature decreases the afferent feedback from the muscles which contributes to activation or increased arousal level. Teaching general relaxation is preparatory toward the other uses of biofeedback such as systematic desensitization.

EMG training is used as part of a protocol for decreasing phobic and anxiety responses. The phobic response originates because of a negative experience that engenders discomfort when dealing with similar experiences due to a pairing of the stimulus with a painful response. As one approaches the feared object, anxiety begins on a low level of awareness. The person chooses to avoid the phobic target, and that reinforces the avoidance response. The first step in desensitization is general relaxation. The next step, seen simply, is to pair the relaxation response with the phobic target so that a new association can be formed: that of relaxation in the face of the feared object.

With anxiety reduction the EMG is used to teach a person how to maintain a relaxed musculature. To trigger the anxiety/arousal response, it is necessary to have a certain level of arousal present. When one is trained to keep the somatic nervous system more relaxed, the anxiety response is less likely to occur.

Essential hypertension is high blood pressure that is not secondary to another condition. The goal in using EMG with essential hypertension is to reduce the muscle contraction that contributes to the pressure in the circulatory system. The essential hypertension protocol pioneered by Fahrion et al. at the Menninger Foundation begins with skin temperature training and combines this with EMG training. The decrease in muscle tension generally decreases the person's tendency to respond to life in a pressured way.

Bruxism is the tendency to grind one's teeth at night. The activity and sound of bruxism are powerful and intense. Bruxism causes the wearing down and loss of teeth as well a misalignment of the jaw and continued problems. The tendency toward bruxism is lessened when biofeedback training encourages reduced contraction of the jaw muscles.

Temporomandibular joint syndrome refers to the misalignment of the jawbone, in which the bone rests loosely in the skull. Many people have their temporomandibular joint poorly positioned, which results in increased muscle tension, increased pain, and increased problems. Some of the headaches people experience as tension headaches are referred pain from the TMJ. With EMG training, the person learns to maintain a resting contraction level that allows the jaw to rest more comfortably in the joint. Such persons also learn to conduct themselves with a more relaxed, poised behavioral style. Contraction of the masseter muscles is an atavistic behavior preparatory to a biting attack, part of the SNS fight-or-flight response. It is almost never appropriate and needs to be decreased as a tendency in favor of increased poise and relaxation. Bilateral EMG feedback of the masseter muscle is the usual protocol.

Neuromuscular re-education in biofeedback is the use of biofeedback instruments to encourage the recruitment of motor units. Muscle electrical activity is enhanced by feeding back the weak signal so that the client is able to get a sense of the effectiveness of his or her attempts to innervate the muscle.

Cerebral palsy is the damage to the brain that occurs either at birth or due to later injury resulting in anoxia (lack of oxygen to the brain). This causes upper motor neuron damage (damage to the part of the motor system from the motor cortex to the spinal cord). This results in the cortex being unable to inhibit the contraction of certain muscles, etc. This inability to inhibit contraction results in the chronic contraction and spasticity of certain muscle groups. The result is uncontrollable spasm and inability to use muscle groups appropriately for particular actions. Typical difficulties include the scissor contraction of leg muscles pulling the legs together or even overlapping them, etc., or chronic contraction of the gastrocnemius which makes it difficult to place the foot for walking. EMG training for cerebral palsy has enabled some clients to be able to find another way to manage the musculature so that necessary movements, feeding, etc., are more possible.

Neuromuscular re-education/stroke is one of the application areas for EMG. It is contrary to the usual direction of behavior shaping of biofeedback. Let's just say that it is more complex. In muscular re-education one is often trying to increase EMG levels rather than decrease them. This means that with feedback of the activity of the few remaining motor units, one is attempting to recruit remaining healthy motor units that may currently be neglected. In the case of stroke, the neural circuits have been temporarily knocked out by the stroke and there is a process which might be referred to as "reminding" them of the learning that they have temporarily lost the capacity to access. When the client is able to see some results of his attempts to innervate the motor units there is increased clarity about what he is doing and more specifically what works for the desired goal.

Stroke rehabilitation works best with the lower extremities. In conjunction with physical and occupational therapy there can be a recovery of function combining the movement patterns that are evoked and reestablished, complete with a sense of progress for even the less available muscle groups. The pattern that is typically used is to begin proximally with the larger muscle groups closer to the body, and with success to move out more distally to the finer muscle groups.

One of the things one may be trying to do is decrease spasticity of the muscle and increase contraction of flaccid muscles. One of the typical goals of neuromuscular re-education is to increase the capacity to dorsiflex the superior surface of the foot. With stroke there is often a difficulty with dorsiflexion, which makes it difficult to walk. With the return of the capacity to dorsiflex, there is the ability to pick the foot up and place it in front without the slight drag that might cause stumbling and decreased self-confidence in walking.

Dysponesis is a concept developed by Whatmore (1974) that refers to misplaced effort. When one contracts a muscle group that is not involved, directly or indirectly, with the activity, or when one contracts the appropriate muscles more than necessary for effective functioning with the task, one experiences dysponesis. Dysponesis is undesirable because it is a great waste of available energy and it even blocks movement in desired directions when a change in position or movement is needed. Range of movement is reduced, and speed of being able to organize the body in a different movement pattern is reduced. Generally, people engaged in dysponesis are not aware of it. With biofeedback they can learn to deploy their energy and contraction patterns more effectively.

One form of dysponesis is bracing. Bracing is the tendency to contract our opposing muscle groups to prepare for experiences or protect against the need for movement. It is a bit like the part of the orienting response that decreases extraneous movement. Bracing can be seen in the EMG/somatic nervous system response; it can also be seen in some people's EDR. For example, if one says to some people, "I am going to ask you a question," one may see this arousal response prior to posing the actual question. This is part of a preparation for the question which has nothing to do with the content of the question itself. Some people brace to protect an injured or formerly injured part of the body.

NEW EMG UTILIZATION AREAS

Two new EMG utilization areas include muscle scanning (developed by Jeffrey Cram) and dynamic EMG. Muscle scanning is the use of small, handheld units (either stand-alone or part of a computer system) placed temporarily over muscles or muscle groups to evaluate the degree of contraction. In this approach, post-type EMG sensors are temporarily placed over the muscle to record its μV levels. The sensor is then moved to another location to record the μV level. Relevant muscles or muscle groups can be scanned quickly to get an overall picture of relative contraction levels.

Dynamic EMG is the use of EMG units (small, portable units, telemetered computer systems, or computer systems with long electrode leads positioned so as to decrease artifact). In dynamic EMG, the term "dynamic" refers to the activity of the client. Regardless of its construction, dynamic EMG is used to monitor the EMG levels of target muscles while one goes about functional daily activities. This is useful in initial evaluations of work or home environments and functional activities; it is particularly useful as one begins to generalize what one has learned in the lab to everyday living. Some people, following their learning of biofeedback skills in the lab, jump into exactly the same misuse of their bodies that brought them to biofeedback in the first place when they resume their ordinary activities. Dynamic EMG facilitates taking the new awareness into the broader range of activities.

BILATERAL EMG TRAINING

It is important in EMG training to train for bilateral symmetry. Bilateral symmetry is comparable EMG readings on the same muscles on both sides of the body. This balance of tonicity enables one to have postural balance. Postural imbalances lead to all kinds of difficulties, including such things as C-scoliosis with its attendant sciatica. Postural imbalances may also restrict range of movement, cause overuse of one side of the body, instigate headaches due to undue muscular contraction on one side, stimulate TMJ syndrome, and perhaps even cause a shifting in function to favor the activities of one hemisphere of the brain since it is habitually more activated.

CHAPTER NINE

ELECTRODERMAL ACTIVITY FEEDBACK (EDA)

"An electrodermal-response biofeedback instrument quantifies and gives one or more feedback indications of the electrical conductivity between two selected contact sites on the skin. . . . Like the peripheral skin temperature 'system,' the electrodermal response (EDR) is mediated by sympathetic nervous system activity. . . ."

KIRK E. PEFFER

"Biofeedback has enabled me to recognize my denial of fear: EDR levels paradoxically high with excellent control of other modalities. This clue is leading me to get a handle on my stress levels."

PHILLIP E. MAUS, BIOFEEDBACKER

Electrodermal activity is a general term which refers to several ways of measuring the electrical characteristics of the skin. EDA can be approached by each of the following methods: skin conductance response (SCR), skin potential (SP), skin conductance level (SCL), and skin potential response (SPR).

Skin conductance level and response are derived by using an instrument that puts out a mild electrical current across the surface of the skin and looks at the degree to which you conduct or resist the flow of electricity. It does not deal directly with the electrical potential differences of your skin. Skin potential (SP) looks at the electrical properties of your skin: the electrical potential difference between one area and another. It is more difficult to measure than SCR and SCL because of the tendency for electrodes to polarize over time which affects the readings. There is research evidence that the SCL of each hand may be inhibited by the contralateral hemisphere of the brain.

A 26-year-old woman was referred to the Novato Institute for biofeedback training. She had been seen by another biofeedback lab and because her baselines were well within the normal range, it was considered that the situation might have more psychological factors and a combination of biofeedback and psychotherapy might be useful. She complained of insomnia and because her measures did not show any elevations beyond normal parameters, it would be difficult to do conventional biofeedback.

As I worked with her, I became aware that the reason she was not sleeping was that she was lying awake thinking of all the things she would like to do in her life, but felt that she couldn't. During the course of her psychotherapy-assisted biofeedback training (using electrodermal feedback modality), she began to realize some of her goals. She was able to go back to school to finish her B.A. She was able to get an exciting job and live in an exciting area. And she began a relationship which eventuated in marriage and a move to another country. Her personal progress was enormous and her insomnia ceased to be a problem.

The goals of EDA training center around enhanced awareness of internal arousal levels so the client learns to realize when he is physiologically stressed and can recognize the need to calm himself.

Many labs do not use EDA. But when a lab does include it with the basic instrumentation, it gives invaluable information to the client and practitioner. Particularly important is the keying in on aspects of the person's life that are particular stressors. EDA can be used to shine a light into every aspect of a person's life to highlight how those elements impact on the person. It can then be used to desensitize the person so that these stressors do not contribute to the person's symptomatology, either psychological or physiological.

Information from the EDA is presented on a moment-by-moment basis. This information is presented either in the form of a unit of measure—resistance (electrical resistance) or ohms—named after one of the pioneers of electricity; or in the form of conductance, measured in micromhos (µmhos) (mho is ohm spelled backwards). These two measures are reciprocals of each other. As you become more resistant, the ohm level goes up and the conductance level (μmho) goes down; as you become more conductant the resistance level goes down.

There are also two other elements in EDA: phasic and tonic changes. Tonic levels refer to the ongoing baseline levels of the EDR. These change relatively slowly. The phasic changes (sometimes referred to as the GSR) are the momentary fluctuations that relate to SNS outflow (anxiety, fear, emotional responses). As one is being recorded, there will be a tonic level baseline, from which there will be sudden elevations (phasic) followed by a return to baseline after the response. How long it takes one to return to baseline depends on the individual nervous system (temperament, personality) and learning (past experience).

GOALS OF EDA TRAINING

EDA training enables you to become more aware of internal arousal levels. With increased awareness, you can notice when you are stressed and can decide whether to decrease your stress levels. After assessing the situation, you can use various interventions to restore homeostasis (Figures 9.1A and 9.1B). This process happens quite rapidly after the learning is integrated. It operates more or less on an unconscious level. One senses that one is becoming stressed by noticing changes in one's physiological state that one has begun to associate with tension. Rapidly, one lets the tension go and moves to another level which is more homeostatically balanced. One may do this either consciously (deliberately) or unconsciously.

GIVING YOUR BODY A VOICE

It is valuable to give your body a voice and to listen to what it has to say on various topics. So often we are going through life experiences, trying desperately to cope, while commanding the body to remain quiet so that no one will recognize our struggle. We even try to fool ourselves. But at times it is valuable to give the body a chance to say "ouch," to allow it to express the fear, anxiety, and distress rather than to swallow them.

I remember working with a client who was processing the death of a relative. The client had not been able to get past it and seemed to be stuck. Monitoring her EDR responses while discussing the situation enabled the client to more thoroughly express the grieving process so that there could be a completion of the process.

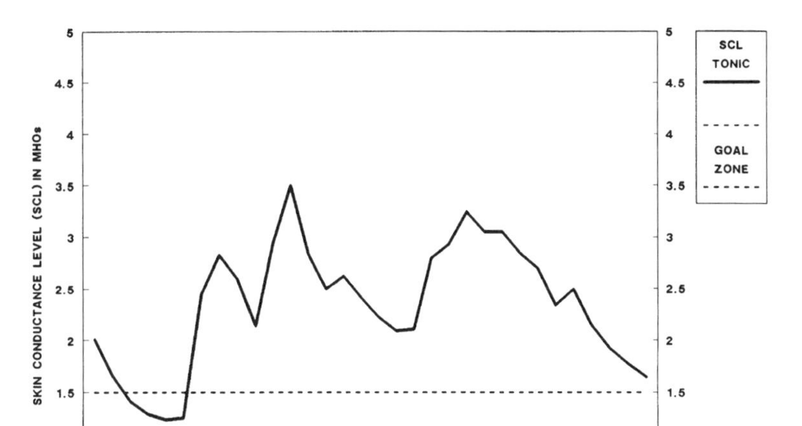

FIGURE 9.1A
Skin conductance level (SCL) in micromhos during the comprehensive evaluation (Client C.C.). Sensors, first and second finger of the right hand, palmar/volar surface.

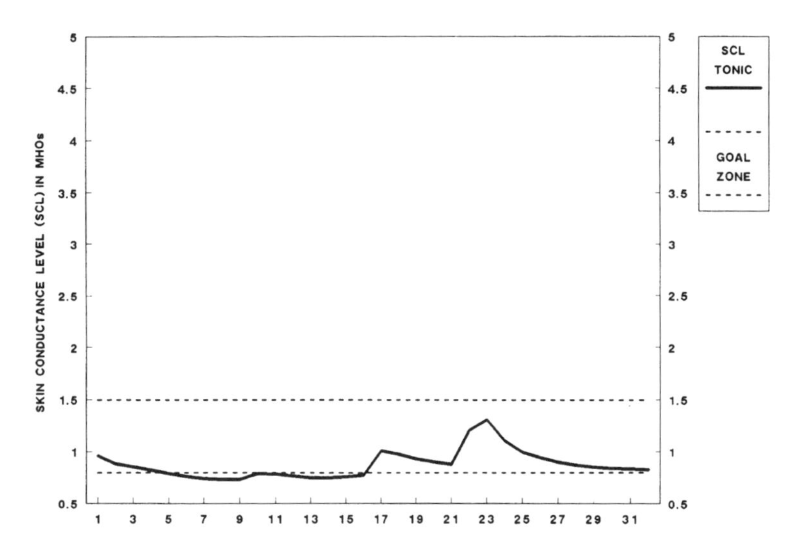

FIGURE 9.1B
Skin conductance level (SCL) levels during session 24 (same client).

ELECTRODERMAL FEEDBACK HISTORY

Generally, there are several key endeavors that are part of the history of electrodermal feedback. These endeavors include the work of Carl Jung, W. D. Fenz and S. Epstein, D. C. Raskin, and others. Electrodermal work has gone through phases of exciting the research and lay population and falling under criticism since the early 1900s.

Carl Jung used the electrodermograph in some of his earlier studies. It is interesting to note in his collected works that he had an experimental interest of a more technological nature. He used the galvanic skin response device to measure physiological changes during the expression of responses in the word association test. The word association test, devised by the Viennese psychoanalyst Sigmund Freud, uses a series of words to elicit responses, which are then examined. The amount of time that it takes to say a word that one associates with the target word is an indication of unconscious processing. For example, if a series of words are read aloud, they might include "table, chair, car, mother . . ." There may be varying amounts of time in the pauses following each word, depending on the reflection and the editing that might go on, indicating deeper-level responses to the words. Most people would pause longer before responding to the word "mother." With the GSR, Jung was able to measure the process that was going on during the responses to key words.

In 1973, Raskin did some research using the GSR in lie detection. The polygraph test, which uses the GSR as part of its battery of tests (GSR, respiration, and heart rate) looks at the physiological response that occurs when a person is lying. It is controversial because not all people have a characteristic response to lying. Some people even have an arousal response to experiencing the polygraph test itself. In fact, the very people that one might want to screen out with the polygraph test might end up as "false negatives." These are the persons with antisocial personality disorders (formerly called sociopaths, psychopaths, etc.). They tend to have a flat GSR with a slow response, decreased level of response, and quick return to baseline. In short, they do not look like they are lying when, in fact, they are. (This may be part of their difficulty. They have never paid the physiological price—anxiety, arousal, physical discomfort—that most people experience when they transgress personal and societal rules. They also seem impulsive and in great need of stimulation which may be a result of their physiological under-arousal.) Fenz and Epstein (1967) used the electrodermograph to research anxiety and stress. For some people, electrodermal activity is a good indicator of anxiety, fear, and stress because they tend to be what has been called by Barbara Brown "skin responders." (Barbara called

EDA "skin talk.") It is associated with anxiety and stress because it is a direct measure of sympathetic nervous system outflow.

PSYCHOPHYSIOLOGY AND TECHNOLOGY OF EDA

To talk about the psychophysiology of the EDA, it is necessary to describe how it works technologically. The EDR (electrodermograph) is an instrument that puts out a mild electrical current from one electrode to another. When you are excited for whatever reason, you will conduct that electrical current more readily. A conductor is a medium that conducts electricity. Good conductors are undistilled water and certain metals (silver and gold, for example). When you are excited, the sympathetic nervous system (SNS) sends out impulses to eccrine glands of the palmar surface of your hands and plantar surface of your feet (Figure 9.2). The eccrine glands then secrete a saline solution unlike the secretions of other sweat glands such as the armpits or other surfaces of the body. Therefore, when the eccrine glands have secreted, you conduct better than when your hands are drier.

The current travels across the surface of the skin and down into the eccrine gland pores. Eventually, it finds its way to the other electrode and the circuit is completed. You are in the electrical circuit, part of the feedback loop.

FACTORS AFFECTING EDR RESPONSE

Both internal and external variables affect EDR response. External factors include age, environmental temperature, recent handwashing, humidity, sudden inhalation, electrodes too tightly or loosely attached, and movement of the client or subject (Venables & Christie, 1973). Internal factors include the intake of nicotine and alcohol (Venables & Christie, 1973).

Various psychological factors also affect the EDR response. They include fear, anger, the startle response, the orienting response, and sexual feelings.

Handwashing before the biofeedback session may result in an elevated EDA baseline due to increased fluid on the surface of the skin. Environmental temperature may cause sweating which will elevate the EDA; humidity will also artificially elevate the EDA as it adds moisture to the skin and helps bridge the electrodes. Age, especially advanced age, may lower the EDA. Persons in the elder years may show a flatter, less responsive EDA due to drying of the skin. Also, people in occupations which expose the hands to chemicals may show a similar decrease in EDA levels. Personality differences and

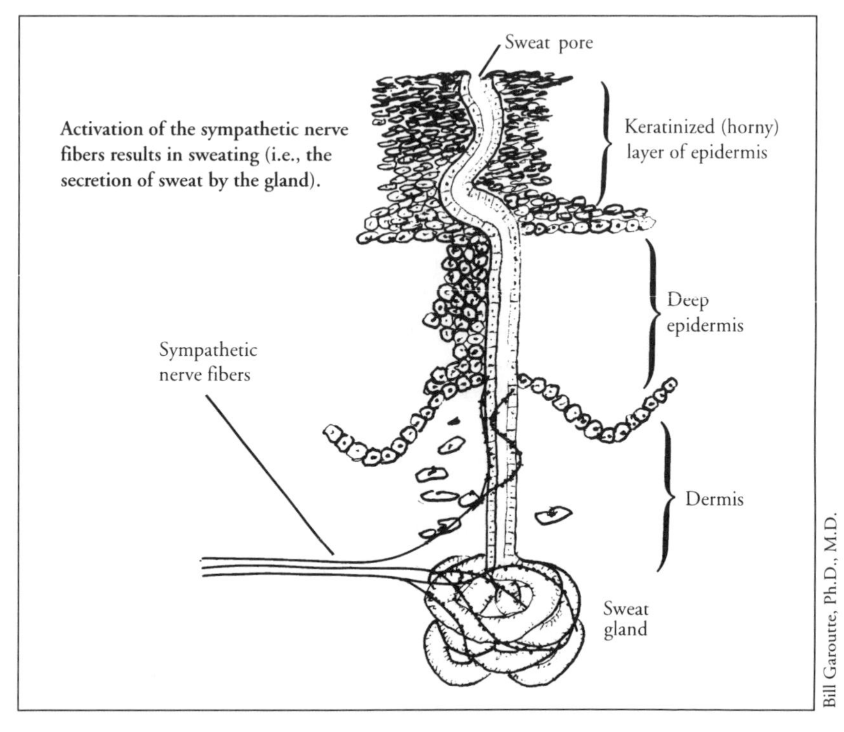

FIGURE 9.2
An eccrine (sweat) gland in the palmar surface of the hand.

psychological states may lower EDA, as in the case of the individual with antisocial personality disorder, who may have a flat EDA, or the depressed person.

Sudden inhalation elevates the EDA briefly and, depending on the client's self-regulation capacities, will vary as to how it affects return to baseline.

Movement will cause a sudden elevation of EDA even if it is a part of the body which does not include the hand being recorded. This is because a physical response causes an arousal reaction which shows itself in more or less whole skin responses.

Pressure against the electrodes comes from the electrodes being put on too tightly or the hand pressing against the electrode, such as against the thigh. This causes sweat gland secretion and also buildup of sweat in the area.

Internal factors such as nicotine may cause a constriction of the peripheral blood vessels, a decrease in skin temperature, and a decrease in sweat gland activity. Alcohol causes an opposite effect. There is a vasodilation, increase in skin temperature, and increase in eccrine gland secretion, not to mention the increased emotionality that accompanies alcohol ingestion.

Fear, anger, startle responses, orienting responses, and sexual feelings (especially initially) all cause a sympathetic nervous system outflow which results in eccrine gland secretion and an elevated EDA.

BEHAVIORAL TESTS

With each of the instruments, after an appropriate hookup has been done, it is necessary to do a behavioral or psychophysiological test. The behavioral test is a maneuver that the trainer instructs the client to do to test the accuracy of the instrument reading. (Accuracy refers to whether the instrument, a standard source, yields a standard reading.) This means that when the client is varied in some way, there is a corresponding and appropriate variation of the instrument's reading. This insures that the practitioner has a good hookup and that the instrument is functioning properly. The behavioral test needs to be done after the hookup and adjustment of the instrument or computer so that the client's readings fall within appropriate scale settings.

For the EDR the behavioral test may include having the client take a sudden inhalation, or the practitioner stroking the client's hand (with permission, of course). There will be a phasic response (usually depending on the client's reactivity). If there is not, then one needs to assess whether it is the client's psychophysiology or whether some aspect of the biofeedback system needs adjusting or is malfunctioning.

APPLICATIONS OF EDA

The EDA can be used in the following ways: 1) as a demonstration tool; 2) to determine characteristic patterns of response; 3) for desensitization (phobias and anxiety); 4) for lowering of sympathetic arousal (hypertension, asthma, stuttering, and hyperhidrosis); and 5) for exploration in psychotherapy, guided imagery and hypnosis (Fuller, 1980).

The EDA may be used to demonstrate the connection between the mind and the body. For example, in giving a lecture, one may hook someone up to the electrodermograph so that the individual or group can see objective indicators of the physiological change that follows a stimulus. For some people, this is (literally) a graphic illustration of the mind/body link, showing that thoughts and behaviors do affect the psychophysiological state. This sudden awareness and insight can help convince the person that care needs to be given to this dimension. The old expression of childhood, "Sticks and stones can break my bones but names can never hurt me" is patently untrue.

For some people, there needs to be a development toward having a greater sense of self-acceptance and self-caring. The biofeedback experience can help foster this attitude. A growing feeling of wanting to care for this precious person (who is you) often comes out of the experience. For some, this is necessary before they will do things to foster health and well-being.

From my observations, self-hatred comes from the disappointments of childhood. It happens at a time when the child feels that his self is rejected, and his magical, powerful potential is wrong in some way that the child cannot understand. This disappointment and infant rage is then turned inward, and the child concludes that he is a "bad person" for ever thinking the wonderful, magical, limitless excitement of the self was valid. The process of beginning to believe in oneself again is a precious, sometimes tearful experience. It is sometimes necessary before one can begin to provide caregiving functions for oneself beyond the minimum necessary for survival.

Other people can find other motivations for engaging in self-care activities such as biofeedback self-care practices. This is sometimes done for the sake of others—family, friends, loved ones—or for the sake of career or work.

The EDA can be used to determine characteristic patterns of response, that is, to show individual differences in characteristic EDA responses. Some people have a rapid, large response that takes a while to return to baseline. Some have a low latency response (response latency refers to how long it takes to respond following a stimulus). It takes everyone from one to two seconds to respond to a stimulus on the electrodermograph because it takes that long to receive the stimulus via the sensory receptors (auditory, visual, or tactile) and for the response to travel down the sympathetic pathway to the eccrine glands to innervate them and cause secretion. Some people do not have much of a phasic response and move back to baseline quickly, while others take longer to respond.

When the electrodermograph is used for desensitization (the training of a new response so that the person ceases to be overreactive), it is often used with phobias and anxiety responses. This process is based on classical conditioning à la Pavlov.

Pavlov discovered that his laboratory dogs began to salivate when someone approached them with meat powder (the dogs were kept slightly hungry for research purposes). Pavlov wanted an explanation for the behavior other than the notion that the dogs were psychic. He decided that the dogs had come to associate the sound of the approaching person with receiving meat. Anyone who has had a pet knows that the mere sound of the refrigerator door opening and food preparation beginning will bring pets forward with the expectation of receiving food.

So Pavlov determined that the original stimulus, which he came to call the unconditioned stimulus (a change in the environmental stimulation which provoked a natural response—the hungry dog responds to the odor or sight of food) provoked a response (salivation in preparation for eating). This original stimulus, when paired with another stimulus which was formerly neutral, began to elicit the same response. The neutral stimulus became the conditioned stimulus (CS) which came to elicit the conditioned response (CR). Eventually, the CS alone elicited the CR. The sound (CS) of the refrigerator door opening will cause salivation (CR).

In the case of phobias, the person has come to have a fear/anxiety response to various environmental stimuli (elevators, bridges, etc.) and has come to avoid them. This has the additional feature of reinforcing the avoided object. It is such a relief not to have to relate to the avoided object that the relief operantly conditions the avoidance behavior.

With the use of EDA, the psychophysiological arousal toward the object is measured and the person can be trained to have a more relaxed response to the object—to be able to approach it, and make a new association between the object and the response. The new response may be one of relaxation, or at least one that does not involve painful arousal. This leads to a new paired association, a new conditioned response.

The EDA can also be used to facilitate the lowering of sympathetic arousal, and to ameliorate the following complaints that are byproducts of such arousal: hypertension, asthma, stuttering, hyperhidrosis (excessive sweating of the hands), etc.

Sympathetic arousal includes the physical changes that are a natural part of the fight or flight response of the SNS. The SNS responds to stressors with an arousal response. The arousal response includes a syndrome set of physiological changes: increased heart rate, increased blood pressure, increased brain wave frequency, decreased skin temperature, etc. The changes are caused by SNS outflow or impulses sent from the posterior hypothalamus down the ganglionic chain beside the spinal cord, to synapse and branch out to the organs or glands innervated by the SNS. Acetylcholine is the transmitter substance at the preganglionic level and epinephrine is the transmitter substance at the end of the pathway at the organ or gland innervated.

The SNS response also includes a more systematic response that involves secretion of epinephrine and norepinephrine by the adrenal medulla into the circulatory system. This has a general, systematic effect of arousing the entire organism. The effect lasts quite a while after the original stimulus, and the chemicals released into the blood remain for a considerable time after secretion.

The EDA, which is a direct measure of SNS activity, is used to flag SNS responses. It is used as a handle on the whole system so that the person can get a sense of when he or she is activating the SNS, how much it is being activated, and what happens when the outflow is lowered. The process may be thought of in terms of applying pressure to the gas pedal of a car—when you step on the gas, the car is supplied with more gasoline that is burned more quickly, and the entire car speeds up. To decrease SNS activity, one must inhibit the outflow, decrease the frequency of impulses being sent out along the SNS pathways.

EDA PROTOCOL

The electrodermograph is used when the client is not too reactive. If the client is too reactive, it will just make him or her more and more aroused, anxious, and hypersensitive. It will take quite a bit of time for the client to calm down, especially if his or her inner critic (called by different names in different theoretical orientations) is involved. The inner critic may be judging the client for exhibiting this reactivity, and for being unable to control his or her physiology and the instrument. "Look at what bad shape you're in. It's probably hopeless." It is particularly important not to do EDA training toward the end of the session, in case the client does not succeed and leaves the session with a feeling of anxiety, distress, failure, or narcissistic injury/shame. People are often amazingly sensitive to how well they do on the instruments. It is amazing because, in a way, the responses they show on the instruments are value-free events. They are simply an indication of where the client is, and perhaps an indication of progress, yet in some instances they take on considerable meaning.

By the same token, the practitioner does not want to do EDA training with someone who has a very flat reading, since not having much to work with may make such a person feel frustrated. Also, the practitioner does not want to further relax such a person in case he or she is suffering from depression (instead, one would want to increase activity). The flat reading may have only to do with relatively low thyroid functioning, genetic makeup, or natural results of the aging process, rather than some condition that warrants any other interpretation. EDA training has marvelous contributions to make toward your feeling more comfortable in the world in all kinds of situations.

CHAPTER TEN

SKIN TEMPERATURE (ST) FEEDBACK TRAINING

"Temperature and/or peripheral blood flow control of the extremities has become one of the major tools of clinical psychologists and their scientific associates."

JOHN V. BASMAJIAN

"In biofeedback training I learned that I could feel safe and relaxed and let my guard down. I didn't have to always be shielding myself from the unexpected. This resulted in increased energy for me and less fatigue."

PATRICIA TROY, BIOFEEDBACKER

Skin temperature feedback uses a thermistor taped to the surface of the hand. The heat of the hand affects the molecules of the thermistor and alters the way the electricity is managed as it comes from and returns to the biofeedback instrument. The thermistor serves as a transducer. It transduces the kinetic energy of the hand's heat into the energetic flow of electricity. This change in electrical flow is processed by the biofeedback instrument and the results are displayed in the form of a meter reading, digital display or other display such as a computer monitor graphing of the moment-by-moment changes of the skin temperature. Most of the ST instruments on the market use Fahrenheit as the unit of measure, but some use celsius.

HISTORY OF SKIN TEMPERATURE FEEDBACK

In 1972, first studies by Sargent, Green and Walters (1972, 1973, 1974) were published. Their research took place at the Menninger Foundation, encouraged by psychologist and author Gardner Murphy. Murphy's idea was to com-

A 60-year-old woman contacted me inquiring about biofeedback. When I saw her I was struck by the seriousness of her condition. Her hands were reddened and the skin of her fingers was shiny and smooth. She said that she had been diagnosed with Raynaud's syndrome and wondered whether biofeedback would help her. We agreed to meet and see if it would. She began with a finger skin temperature of 71 degrees Fahrenheit. Her ST was quite labile, which is typical of clients with a vasomotor condition. For example, she was able to increase the temperature of her hands 14 degrees Fahrenheit in one session. We used ST training to teach her to elevate the hand temperature.

She learned to be more aware of her hands in all situations, wearing gloves when necessary, and avoiding cold situations such as washing vegetables in cold water. She practiced her autogenic-like suggestions at home faithfully at least once a day.

She was able to avoid extreme Raynaud's episodes and when she could not, she was able to decrease the severity.

bine autogenic training suggestions, originated by Schultz and Luthe, with temperature biofeedback. The researchers used the combination of skin temperature feedback with autogenic suggestions in single case reports with migraine headache clients. Their research has been criticized for not using adequate controls, but their work nevertheless provided landmark information.

In the development of any field, it is at first important to publish the findings that suggest an effect. Later, the research (with the help of appropriate critique and feedback from other professionals) refines its designs and statistical measures. Some critics of biofeedback have used these and other studies to undermine the significance of the findings, but the studies only represent a natural point in the evolution of the field.

In 1974, A. Steptoe et al. found that significant differences in earlobe temperature could be created by subjects using visual and auditory feedback. Ian Wickramsekera used a combination of biofeedback and no treatment baseline conditions in 1973 with two migraine headache clients. The first condition was frontalis EMG for 18 sessions. The second condition was a no-treatment baseline. This was followed by hand temperature training. This is reportedly the first clinical application using combined modalities.

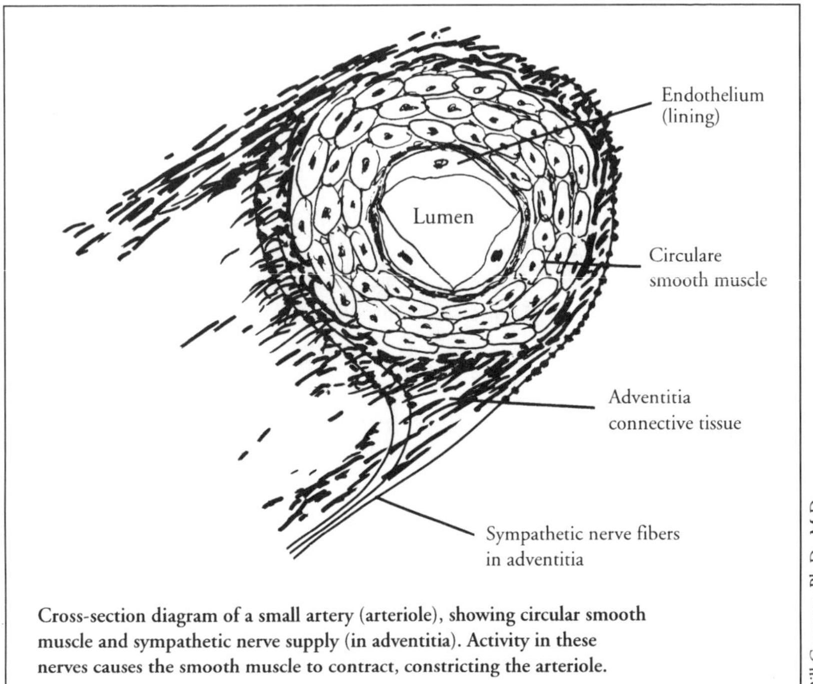

Cross-section diagram of a small artery (arteriole), showing circular smooth muscle and sympathetic nerve supply (in adventitia). Activity in these nerves causes the smooth muscle to contract, constricting the arteriole.

FIGURE 10.1
Smooth muscle found in the wall of the blood vessel.

The first reported use of temperature training with Raynaud's syndrome patients was by Surwit in 1973. He published evidence of temperature training protocol for Raynaud's syndrome. His four patients demonstrated improvement.

In addition to the other researchers mentioned above, A. Turin and W. G. Johnson (1976) studied seven migraine headache patients in an effort to address the criticism of the earlier work.

PHYSIOLOGY OF ST

Peripheral temperature is a function of the degree of contraction of the peripheral blood vessels. The contraction of the blood vessels, called the vasomotor response, is under the control of the sympathetic nervous system. The contraction is accomplished when sympathetic nervous system impulses are conducted to the smooth muscles in the walls of the vessels (Figure 10.1). Impulses along the sympathetic pathways finally cause a constriction of the blood vessels. This reduces the amount of blood flow to the area and thus reduces skin temperature. There will also be a paling of the skin with the reduction of blood flow to the area.

With an increase in arousal level, there is an increase in sympathetic nervous system outflow. This constricts the peripheral blood flow and helps shunt the blood toward the striated muscles and the brain for emergency responses. With ST feedback the individual is able to warm his or her hands by decreasing the sympathetic outflow. This allows the blood vessels to dilate or relax. Blood flow is then increased toward the periphery (Figures 10.2A and 10.2B).

Skin temperature varies due to a number of factors. One factor is the fluctuations in internal or core body temperature. Environmental temperature also affects skin temperature. Finally, vasomotor activity will affect skin temperature. Vasomotor activity may be the result of emotion or response of the organism that causes a sympathetic nervous system outflow.

Biochemical factors may also influence peripheral skin temperature. The presence of carbon dioxide will decrease peripheral skin temperature. Lactic acid produced by muscle activity will affect skin temperature by elevating it. Histamine will increase peripheral temperature. Ephedrine will decrease peripheral skin temperature. Nicotine in tobacco will decrease peripheral skin temperature. Anxiety and emotional stress will cause vasoconstriction of the peripheral vessels.

There is a clinical picture of a person who somaticizes his stress response in the autonomic nervous system. This person tends to be highly emotionally sensitive. He has a concern with his self-image and the acceptance of others. He also has a habit of worrying overmuch about little events.

VASOMOTOR RESPONSE

The vasomotor control mechanisms enable the body to regulate its responses to environmental temperature changes. By constriction or dilation of the smooth muscles around the peripheral blood vessels, there can be an increase or decrease of blood flow to the extremities. A decrease in blood flow to the periphery allows for an increase in blood flow to the internal organs. This allows the body to maintain a constant core temperature.

The vasomotor response is primarily the result of the sympathetic nervous system (SNS). Impulses from the SNS cause a constriction of smooth muscles

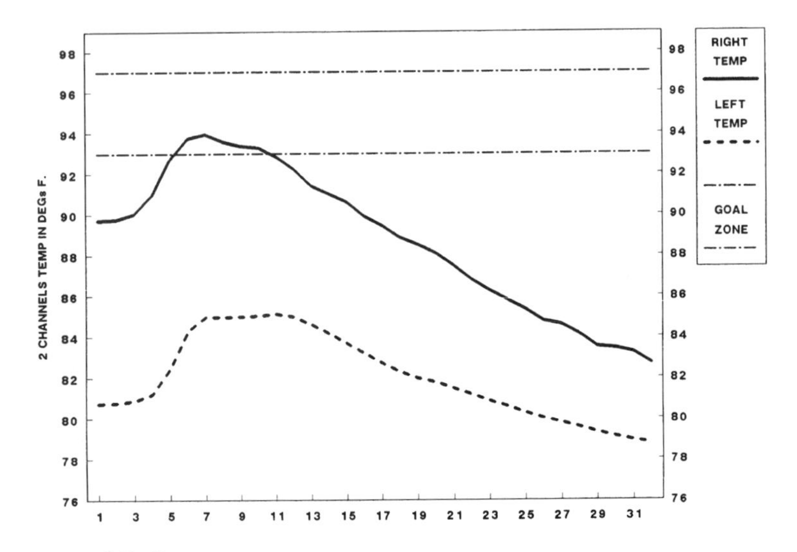

FIGURE 10.2A
Right and left hand temperatures during the 32-minute comprehensive evaluation; Client C.C. (Thermistor is placed on the ring fingers of the right and left hands, volar surface.)

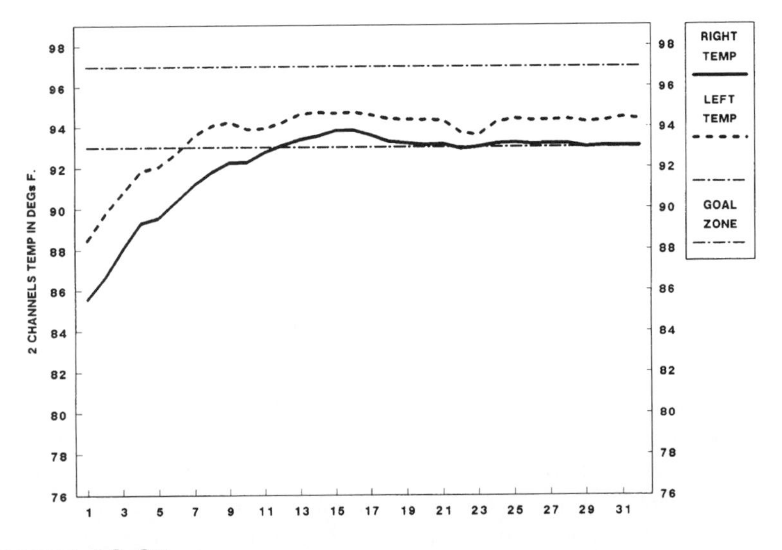

FIGURE 10.2B
Right and left hand temperature during session 24 (Client C.C.).

of the blood vessels. This allows for an increase in blood flow to the brain, muscles, and spinal cord. It prepares the person to run or to fight.

CORE TEMPERATURE VERSUS PERIPHERAL TEMPERATURE

There is a difference between core temperature and peripheral temperature. Core temperature is the internal body temperature, and is approximately 98.6 degrees Fahrenheit. There are some individual variations, but that is considered normal. Peripheral temperature, on the other hand, is the temperature measured on the surface of the skin. Ambient or room temperature affects peripheral temperature. Core temperature also affects peripheral temperature. As a rule, peripheral temperature remains somewhere below core temperature. Peripheral temperature is the result of the vasomotor changes discussed above.

SKIN TEMPERATURE PSYCHOPHYSIOLOGY

The psychophysiological mechanisms of ST changes include the following: The SNS sends impulses out along neurons to contract the smooth muscles of the blood vessels. As the smooth muscles of the arterioles contract there is a decrease in blood flow to the periphery. The blood supply is redirected or shunted to the brain, spinal cord, and muscles. This is part of the preparation for fighting or running. As the blood decreases its flow through the peripheral pathways, there is a decrease in surface skin temperature.

Blood is warm, and the kinetic energy of its flow also contributes to its warmth. As one decreases the flow to an area, there is a cooling trend.

THERMISTOR ATTACHMENT AND LOCATION

The thermistor, usually a heat sensitive resister (it may also be constructed with a microchip) is attached to the hand in a variety of locations, depending on preference. There are no hard data to support the placement on one location versus another. The sensor may be placed on the palmar surface of a finger, the outer border of a finger, the nail bed of a finger, or the palm of the hand. Different practitioners and manufacturers recommend different locations.

The most important factor is consistency between session to session with the same person. There are variations in responsiveness of different areas among different people. To change locations from session to session without an adequate rationale and documentation of changed electrode placement means that the practitioner and client will be comparing and making judgments that may be spurious. It is a bit like comparing apples and oranges.

EXTERNAL AND INTERNAL VARIABLES THAT AFFECT ST

Both external and internal variables affect ST. External sources include the ambient temperature, both in the outer environment and within the room. The internal factors come from what the person has eaten or drunk prior to the session. For example, alcohol is a vasodilator. Nicotine is a vasoconstrictor. Sometimes, as in the case of medication, it is not possible to eliminate the cause of artificially elevated ST. In that case, one must take into consideration the fact that there is an added element contributing to ST responses.

Lactic acid, a byproduct of muscle contraction, causes a vasodilation and increased temperature of the extremities. (For example, following unusual exertion such as mowing the lawn or working in the yard, the next day you will feel sore and somewhat warmer than usual, you are aware of the vasodilation effects of increased lactic acid.) Increased carbon dioxide causes a decrease in vasoconstriction and has a cooling effect, while caffeine, a stimulant, stimulates vasodilation.

PSYCHOLOGICAL FACTORS AND ST

Psychological factors also affect skin temperature. Among them are emotional stress, fear, anxiety, and the response to environmental stimuli. These are essentially sympathetic nervous system responses which cause vasoconstriction. When ST is monitored, fluctuations in response to changes in the person's psychological state during conversation and behavior may be seen. These responses may be positive or negative. Negative responses are obvious, but the changes that accompany other moods such as excitation may not be so obvious.

BEHAVIORAL TEST FOR SKIN TEMPERATURE BIOFEEDBACK

After the thermistor is attached to the client's hand, and the instrument has been turned on and stabilized, the practitioner can touch the thermistor. The temperature reading will increase or decrease depending on the temperature difference between the two hands.

APPLICATIONS OF THERMAL BIOFEEDBACK

Thermal biofeedback has become the standard application for several conditions. Within the field of biofeedback it has become the treatment of choice for these conditions. (In the field of medicine, thermal biofeedback is becoming the treatment of choice for a couple of these conditions. Physicians are increasingly referring patients to biofeedback for these conditions.) The conditions are migraine headaches, Raynaud's disease, hypertension, and asthma episodes (Fuller, 1980).

Migraine Headaches Migraine headaches are headaches that are described as being mainly one-sided. Later stages of the headache may give the experience of pain on both sides of the head. They are episodic; they are intermittent. The aura or prodromal symptoms are sensations that the person has found to reliably signal the onset of the headache. They include scintillating scotomas (flashing lights). The individual experiencing the prodromal symptoms may stop what he or she is doing and do a relaxation procedure to stop the incoming stimulation and impose a parasympathetic nervous system dominance to counter the rising sympathetic nervous system response. Migraine headaches often follow a period of relaxation, during the time that the cranial arteries are constricted. When this period is followed by a stressor that suddenly causes a dilation of the cranial vessels, this causes a stretching of the pain receptors which stimulates them and results in pain.

Migraine sufferers have certain personality characteristics associated with the condition. Such persons tend to be intelligent, hard working, conscientious, meticulous, etc. When such people learn self-regulation practices, they have a struggle deciding to stop what they are doing when the prodromal symptoms let them know that a migraine is on its way. Because they are so conscientious, they want very much to continue the task or tasks in which they are engaged. Therefore, they need a number of experiences of paying attention to the prodromal symptoms and stopping to abort the headache before they can generalize these procedures regularly into their everyday lives.

Migraine headaches are vascular in nature. The theory and observation of migraine headaches suggests that there is a change in dilation of the blood vessels serving the head. There are two kinds of migraine headaches: common and classical. The classical migraine is a headache that is preceded by prodromal symptoms, which vary from person to person depending on what area of the brain has been starved for blood flow due to constriction of the blood vessels and then suffused with the sudden dilation of the blood vessels. The classical migraine is usually one-sided. There is a throbbing, and sensitivity to light and sound. There may be vomiting and the need to lie down. The migraine varies in frequency, intensity, and duration. This is true of other headaches as well.

The original conception of how biofeedback was effective with migraine headaches had to do with shunting the blood flow from the head/brain to the periphery of the body. With SNS activation there is an increase in blood to the CNS and muscles. This is the well-known fight-or-flight response.

It has been observed that it is difficult, if not impossible, to abort a migraine headache once it has begun. But if one stops at the first sign of prodromal symptoms, one is able to abort the impending headache. This becomes quite a challenge for the person with migraine headaches. When the prodromal syndrome begins, there is a conflict between going on with the goal-directed activities, or stopping to take time to abort the headache. There is often a sorting-out process in which the person learns that it is not worth it to pursue the schedule and risk the negative consequences.

Raynaud's Disease Raynaud's disease is another presenting problem with which ST has been effective. Raynaud's disease patients show a tendency for the peripheral blood vessels to constrict. The chronic condition can be quite serious, with difficulty in healing and sometimes gangrene. Gangrene necessitates the amputation of part of the fingers or toes.

The symptoms of Raynaud's disease include a decrease in skin temperature due to decreased blood flow to the periphery. This also shows itself in blanching of the hands and cyanosis (blueing of the fingers). This is followed by an intense reddening of the area as blood returns to the hands and fingers.

Several environmental and psychophysiological factors trigger the Raynaud's response. The psychophysiological factors include anxiety, emotional responses, etc. The environmental factors include cold weather and touching cold objects (e.g., washing vegetables in cold water, holding cold drinks).

The person with Raynaud's disease needs to learn how to protect the hands with gloves when necessary and how to warm them internally through self-regulatory practices.

The protocol for working with Raynaud's disease includes teaching the person how to warm the hands using temperature feedback and a variety of strategies for facilitating the warming trend. Autogenic suggestions are particularly helpful in fostering the hand-warming response.

It is particularly important for the Raynaud's patient to become increasingly aware of hand temperature responses and keep up a regular daily practice of hand warming to maintain a warmer baseline. It is said that a bottom line temperature of 72 degrees Fahrenheit needs to be held, and anything below this is to be greatly discouraged. This is approximately room temperature.

Hypertension A biofeedback application that has received a lot of research attention is hypertension (high blood pressure). Hypertension is of two basic types: idiopathic hypertension, and hypertension that results from another condition, such as atherosclerosis. Hypertension may also be labile (fluctuating) or essential (stable in its above-normal levels).

Conservative medical treatment includes dietary recommendations such as reduced salt intake and pharmacological measures such as antihypertension medications. The medication may have side effects, including depression (particularly in males) and impotence. There is also the difficulty that may arise when hypertension is not controlled even by high dosages of medication.

Therefore, a nonpharmacological approach to blood pressure control is valuable. Biofeedback is just such an intervention. Biofeedback has been addressing blood pressure, somewhat indirectly, for a number of years. The original approach to the use of biofeedback with hypertension was EMG training. The theory was that muscle contraction levels had an impact on blood pressure, and that a reduction of EMG levels would help lower blood pressure. While this is helpful, the contemporary approach fostered by Steven Fahrion and others of the Menninger Foundation begins with temperature training followed by EMG training. The protocol includes training ST to criterion (95 degrees) in the hands and then the feet.

Asthma Biofeedback has been used in the treatment of asthma episodes. Asthma is a medical condition characterized by a difficulty in getting adequate oxygen. It is caused by constriction of the bronchioles. There is some question as to whether is it caused by a physiological agent or a psychological component. Regardless, after the individual has had it for a long time, there is a great deal of learned behavior contributing to the condition. It is important to combine biofeedback treatment of asthma with respiratory therapy.

The biofeedback skill is not used during the asthma episode, since the relaxation response is associated with PNS activation, which further constricts the bronchioles. Medication is often used to dilate the bronchioles. Biofeedback can be helpful in reducing the frequency of asthma episodes and helping the person scan the environment for triggers of asthma episodes. Having flagged stressors, the person can work to desensitize, change, and modify the stressors. So there are two contributions from biofeedback: creating a general relaxation state on a maintenance basis and removing unnecessary stressors from the environment. There is an additional element which can give the person a sense of control: increased self-efficacy, which is an important aspect of all medical and psychological recovery or coping capacities.

Another useful approach besides combining biofeedback with respiratory therapy is the family therapy approach. This approach, developed by Erik Peper and others, emphasizes the family system involvement in the condition. Therefore, when the person with asthma is doing respiratory exercises, it is valuable for the whole family to participate in the process.

Temperature Training in Psychotherapy Like EDA training, temperature training can be used as an adjunct to psychotherapy. The vasomotor system is very responsive to nervous system responses to internal and external experiences. If one monitors temperature changes over a period of time, one will be surprised to see just how responsive the vasomotor system is. During a period of time in the lab and during conversation, fluctuation parallels the topics discussed and shows sympathetic nervous system outflow in response to the topics. The hands will cool with SNS activation, which represents excitement (either positive or negative). There may even be a difference in hand temperatures, reflecting differentiation between right and left hemisphere activation.

Strategies The purpose of increasing peripheral skin temperature is to decrease SNS outflow. This is done by decreasing the number impulses going out to constrict the smooth muscles of the blood vessels. There are various strategies to bring this about, and their effectiveness varies from person to person. These strategies make use of different parts of the brain and go about it in slightly different ways. It is important to try different strategies with the aid of biofeedback to see which ones are most effective.

The typical strategies include autogenic suggestions (such as "My hands are heavy, warm and limp"); visualizing oneself in a warm environment, such as warm sunlight at the beach or by a warm fire; enhancing kinesthetic sensations toward a feeling of increased warmth; imagining increased blood flow to the hands and feet; and others.

Autogenic training suggestions can be formal, in which one goes systematically through the body to suggest that each part is warm, heavy, and limp, or more informal, focusing on the hands and suggesting that they are warm and heavy. Visualization and imagery can be also be general (imagining warm scenes) or specific (visualizing blood flowing to the extremities).

Once you have learned how to elevate your peripheral temperature using biofeedback, you can use that technique without instrumentation, using your demonstratively effective strategy, for relaxation and continued effective performance in everyday situations.

CHAPTER ELEVEN

ADJUNCTIVE PROCEDURES

"The practitioner, whether his discipline be clinical psychology, psychiatry or physical medicine, will find that knowledge of relaxation techniques will have many applications in his daily work. . . ."

JOHANN M. STOYVA

"I found that using autogenic training was one of the fastest ways to fairly dramatically increase my skin temperature. I also found that I experienced an overall sense of relaxation, that was reflected in the numbers. At first I had my trainer read the suggestions to me. This worked well, but I wanted to try suggesting to myself, so that I could use autogenic training when I was alone. It worked almost as well as when the suggestions came internally. I have since used autogenic training in my home practice and subjectively I found good results."

HALIMAH MCLAUGHLIN, BIOFEEDBACKER

"Biofeedback is extremely useful for integrating the mind/body and spirit. The biofeedback process helps one become aware of the way stress is carried in each individual's body. Once the location of the stress is discovered, work can be done on releasing old negative patterns for imbalance in the body."

SUSAN WARD, BIOFEEDBACKER

Biofeedback has been determined through numerous studies to be efficacious. Statistical significance has shown that it works. Numerous studies have combined biofeedback with other relaxation practices, usually showing that biofeedback works even better in combination with other procedures. In fact, the other procedures work quite well without biofeedback, and some may be tempted to ask, why bother with biofeedback? The answer is, because it provides precision.

The adjunctive procedures have a long history separate from biofeedback, and are not adjunctive to their own realities. They include progressive relaxation, heterohypnosis (other-hypnosis) and autohypnosis (self-hypnosis), suggestion, guided visualization and imagery, meditation and quasi-meditation, autogenic training, systematic desensitization, cognitive restructuring, etc.

ALTERED STATES OF CONSCIOUSNESS

Biofeedback training, although we are not as aware of it at this time in history, is a means toward altering consciousness. When we experience an altered state of consciousness (ASC), there is the implication that special things can happen.

Biofeedback training is similar to hypnosis in that you are asked to reduce sensory input and motor input, to narrow your focus of attention to include only the trainer's voice and/or the feedback signal (auditory or visual).

It is very important that trainers watch what they say because the client may be very suggestible and receptive in the altered state. This means that the patter that is part of the fabric of the biofeedback experience needs to be consistent with the goals of training. The way the trainer discusses home practice needs to exclude chance statements, such as "You will probably have trouble fitting this into your busy schedule, but try," and include enabling statements, such as "With practice, you will become more and more able to self-regulate your body's responses to stress."

RESULTS OF ADJUNCTIVE PROCEDURES

Biofeedback gives the client an opportunity to see the results of adjunctive self-regulation practice. The feedback and data, in the beginning, are a little distracting. This is particularly true if the client has been used to doing a meditation practice without feedback. In each practice, instructions are given to the body or physiology, and the nervous system goes about making the changes in ways we can only speculate. The biofeedback instrument enables us to see the degree to which we have been successful.

HYPNOSIS AND BIOFEEDBACK

Hypnosis is the grandparent of all the adjunctive techniques. Although it has probably existed throughout the ages, Anton Mesmer introduced it in the 1700s to western Europe under the name of animal magnetism. He used magnets to pass over the body while he talked to the client. Probably, the effect of passing magnets across the energy field of the body had some effect on the client. Later, he tried to move beyond that to magnetize water, etc.

Mesmer was also engaged in suggestions of conscious and unconscious kinds. Later, the process was called hypnosis, and it has had a checkered history. I think it is fascinating to realize that some of the principles regarding the hypnotic experience remain truisms even today. It was noticed even then that a rapport developed between the hypnotist and the client. Certain principles developed to give the hypnotist some ethical constraints as they handled this very special situation between human beings.

Hypnosis has been defined as an enhanced state of suggestibility. It may be induced by another person or situation ("heterohypnosis") or by oneself ("autohypnosis"). Bodily relaxation is an important first step. A second step is concentration on a narrowed set of stimuli. Your focus of attention becomes greatly restricted.

Not everyone is susceptible to hypnosis, and the degree of susceptibility varies.

The term hypnosis refers to the original conception that the hypnotic state was a sleep state. It is named for the Greek god of sleep, Hypnos. We now know that hypnosis is not a sleep state, since the brain waves are not characteristic of sleep.

It has been suggested that hypnosis confuses the left side of the brain, or talks it into decreasing activation, allowing the right hemisphere to be more dominant. Indications for this include the client's decreased capacity and willingness to talk and altered sense of time and reality that are suggestive of right hemisphere activity. EEG research findings from Hilgard and others show slight increases of right hemisphere activity during hypnosis.

Although there are aspects of the biofeedback process which are hypnosis inducing, there is a point at which a deeper level of hypnosis is no longer biofeedback. At certain levels of trance the client can no longer experience biofeedback because he or she can no longer hear or respond to the feedback signal. At this point the person may be deeply relaxed, but is no longer engaged in biofeedback.

There are four basic steps in the induction stage of hypnosis. The four steps include 1) a decrease in sensory input and motor output; 2) focusing of attention; 3) repetition of the stimulation; and 4) establishment of rapport between the subject and hypnotist or hypnotherapist.

Actually, these four steps apply to all the self-regulatory procedures. Limitation of sensory input and motor output relates to the general procedure of asking the person to sit quietly and clear his or her mind. The amount of light in the room is also generally reduced, and things are kept as quiet as possible. The trainer speaks in a calm, quiet voice, and the conversation is restricted to certain suggestions and responses, unlike ordinary conversation which ranges all over the place from topic to topic. Attention is fixed on a particular target—perhaps the voice of the hypnotist, or a visual target upon which the hypnotist directs the client to focus, such as a pen held in the client's hand. Repetition of monotonous stimulation usually consists of the hypnotist's voice, but the visual target or another sound can be repetitive as well. The rapport between the client and hypnotist develops out of the lowered arousal level and lowering of ego boundaries, resulting in a greater degree of intimacy.

The hypnosis session usually begins with a discussion. The purpose of the discussion is to establish rapport. The client is reassured that hypnosis susceptibility is not an indication of psychological problems or low intelligence. The hypnotist attempts to convince you that you will not do anything against your will or against your ethical code.

It is important to remember that this last statement is both true and untrue. It is true that the person being hypnotized will not do anything that he or she would not normally do. But the hypnotist can suggest an altered context in which the person would do what he or she would not do outside of the altered context. For example, one would not ordinarily jump out of a window, but if the hypnotist realistically suggested that the building was on fire and all other means of escape were blocked, and the person needed to save his or her life and perhaps the lives of his or her children, that person might be willing to jump out of the window. In the case of group hypnosis, a kind of mass hysteria can even move a group to suicide (as in the case of Jim Jones convincing many people to drink a poisoned soft drink).

It is important to remember that human beings, like other animals, are vulnerable to suggestion and hypnosis. This means that we must remain alert to possible misuses and that we make rational choices as to when to use this very powerful and (at its best) helpful tool.

There are tests for assessing the effect of suggestions or deepening the trance level. The purpose of these tests is to let the hypnotist know to what degree the client is entranced, and to allow the client to get a sense of the degree to which he is in a trance (in a special state of consciousness in which special things are possible that are not possible under ordinary circumstances). The trance state allows one to gain a new sense of possibilities for the future, and allows one to trust the state and be more receptive to it when one is hypnotized the next time. Suggestions for the future that are implanted during the trance prepare the person for the use of his or her capacities at a later date; for example, one may receive suggestions about childbirth without anesthesia.

The tests of trance level include 1) suggestion that you will be unable to open your eyes (you are given the paradoxical suggestion to try to open your eyes, but you will find that you are not able to open them); 2) suggestion that your response to a stimulus will change ("hyperthesia" is the term for increasing your response to sensations; "anesthesia" is the term for decreasing your response); 3) suggestion of amnesia (for example, the hypnotist may tell you to imagine a blackboard and to write a statement on the blackboard. Then the hypnotist suggests that you are unable to see or remember the words. Finally, you are told that you can see or remember them again); 4) post-hypnotic suggestions given during the trance to be carried out after the trance (in trance, you are told that you will not remember the suggestion. A classic example is that you will open a window); 5) suggestions of positive or negative hallucinations (a positive hallucination is that something or someone has been brought into the room and a negative hallucination is that something or someone has been removed from the room). The hypnotist does not usually go through all these tests. They are also approaches to deepening the trance level.

There are several kinds of hypnotists. They include hypnotists, hypnotherapists, hypnoanalysts, hypnosis trainers, etc. The hypnotist is most concerned with symptom removal. There are a few intervening steps before the suggestion of the removal of the unwanted symptom or behavior. Behaviors may also be added to one's life through hypnosis; for example, one might allow oneself to be more able to write in the case of writer's block or become more creative.

Because it is so symptom oriented, the issue of symptom substitution becomes a concern when using hypnosis.

Medical Applications of Hypnosis Hypnosis is used for relieving various symptoms. It has been used with asthma, chronic skin diseases, diabetes, eating disorders (especially overeating), insomnia, and other presenting complaints. Tendencies toward spontaneous abortions and functional sterility have been aided with hypnosis. Chronic pain clients have been helped with hypnosis procedures such as general relaxation and "glove" anesthesia. Hypnosis has also been used in presurgical preparation of patients by anesthesiologists and others.

Situations of high stress and distress, such as emergency room situations, panic episodes, dissociative states (for example, fugues, somnambulism, and the like), and combat-induced states are also suggestible states receptive to hypnotic suggestions.

Hypnosis has also been used with recurring hiccuping, anorexia and other eating disorders, and psychogenic vomiting (for example, bulimia and performance anxiety responses).

Dental hypnosis may be used to relax clients with anxiety and phobia in dental situations, and for pain reduction. It may be used to help in the acceptance of dental appliances or to help with dental related habits such as nail biting and temporomandibular joint problems such as bruxism or teeth grinding. Some dental patients are allergic to anesthesiology procedures and require alternate pain management techniques.

Under hypnosis there is an attitude and approach which is very positive and facilitating. A useful metaphor for expressing this is "all roads lead to Rome." When guiding a person with hypnotic suggestions, whatever he or she does is considered or treated as though it is a means toward the desired behavior. For example, if the hypnotist says "Your eyes are feeling heavy and you will soon be closing them" and it looks as though the client is not ready to comply with the suggestion, the hypnotist can use the noncompliance as a way of moving toward the suggestion: "As your eyes remain open a little longer, you are preparing for the next stage of allowing them to close more easily."

Resistance is also met another way if the client has told the therapist that he or she wishes to accomplish a goal (a conscious desire) and then signals through ideomotor movements (slight muscle twitches, for example, small finger movements) that he or she is not ready to do this. Time distortion may be used to bring the date in the future (at which point achievement of the goal will be possible) closer to the present.

SUGGESTION

As in hypnosis, suggestion plays direct and indirect roles in biofeedback. For example, there is direct suggestion that is used by the trainer as he or she guides the client through the procedure. Indirectly, it occurs through the "demand characteristics" of the situation. Suggestion is a subtle part of every aspect of the biofeedback experience. Just as there are very clear and obvious suggestions in the situation, so too there are many suggestions embedded in every aspect of the situation.

Therefore, the biofeedbacker is very concerned about the suggestions involved in each situation. He or she is concerned that the environment suggest the kind of state that is being taught. He or she is also concerned about saying things that are congruent with the state and way of being that is being taught. It is important that the trainer's message be clear, and that he or she does not inadvertently include mixed messages of double binds, such as "You are probably not going to find time to do home practice, but at a time like this it is especially important."

AFFIRMATIONS

Affirmations are a form of suggestion. They are popular with certain groups in different parts of the world, and have been since 1900 and before. In an informal way, they have been around since the dawn of human awareness. Affirmations may be defined as statements about one's behavior and situations that create an intention and imply the development of possibilities. They have become increasingly popular in recent years as people have become concerned with enhancing their health and behavior. They include the original, world-renowned affirmation by Couè, "Every day in every way I am becoming better and better." They have become commercialized through cards, calendars, stickers, etc. One can keep these in sight and mind to remind oneself of the state of mind, attitude, or behavior that one is trying to incorporate in one's life. Affirmations may be done visually, imagistically, and verbally.

In selecting affirmations, you need to choose statements that are compatible with your way of expressing yourself. They need to be open ended rather than stating the desired attitude or behavior as a completed achievement. For example, it is better to say, "I am becoming healthier" rather than "I am healthy." Affirmations are a way of programming one's biocomputer.

AUTOGENIC TRAINING

Developed by Wolfgang Luthe and J. H. Schultz in Germany in the 1920s, autogenic training (AT) is a treatment for stress-related conditions. It was Gardner Murphy, the famous psychologist and author, who suggested to Elmer and Alyce Green that they use autogenic training suggestions with temperature training for migraine headache clients in 1965. The contraindications for autogenic training are similar to the list for biofeedback.

Autogenic training is a hypnosis-like procedure. "Autogenic" means self-generating. The purpose of the exercises is to deal with stress-related disorders. The story goes that the training was an adaptation of hypnosis procedures that would avoid the negative attitudes toward hypnosis and decrease resistance to its use. It was designed to be used within the medical community.

Autogenic training exercises can be taught as the home practice exercise of choice. They can be used to facilitate the biofeedback learning process. Autogenic training is particularly effective with skin temperature training.

Different people are drawn toward different relaxation exercises. Sometimes one starts out with certain relaxation exercise preferences and then others start to become significant because new insights arise regarding presenting problems and other issues one might wish to address.

Autogenic training consists of levels of exercises. Biofeedback practitioners may use a classic form of AT with their biofeedback training and as home practice assignments, or a more informal version in which some of the same principles are embedded.

AT has an advantage over hypnosis in that is it not just helpful for symptom removal, but suggests physiological changes that one can use to achieve particular states.

The exercises are aimed to produce six standard sensations and states: limb heaviness, peripheral warmth, reduced heart rate, regular respiration, visceral regulation, and forehead cooling (Fuller, 1977). It is necessary to use passive volition, trying without trying, when doing these exercises. Somatic awareness is focused and specific sensations are induced to encourage homeostasis. The procedures apparently operate to reduce sympathetic nervous system outflow.

Limb heaviness suggests decreases in somatic nervous system activity. Peripheral warmth suggests vasodilation of the periphery or a decrease in sympathetic nervous system outflow to contract the smooth muscles of the peripheral blood vessels. Reduction of heart rate decreases SNS outflow to the heart along the vagus nerve. Visceral regulation is also a PNS function. Forehead cooling further emphasizes the warming of the periphery and decreases in blood flow to the heart, scalp, etc.

During these suggestions, made by the practitioner and repeated by the client, the attitude of passive volition is cultivated. Passive volition roughly means trying without trying—intending an activity but making it happen by not trying, and instead enabling it or allowing it to happen. It involves a kind of relaxing into the response, focusing somatic awareness and inducing specific sensations. With relaxation and focusing awareness on somatic functions, there is a shift away from SNS dominance toward PNS dominance. Homeostasis is facilitated.

PROGRESSIVE RELAXATION

Edmund Jacobson, a Harvard educated physician (1908), developed progressive relaxation in the 1930s. Jacobson did a considerable amount of his work at the University of Chicago. He developed a system to teach comprehensive skeletal muscle relaxation using a combination of active and passive volition.

In progressive relaxation, there is a volition, a willing, an intention, which is achieved both actively by voluntary movement and passively through the nonvoluntary sensing of movements. The client contracts and then quickly relaxes various muscles or muscle groups. This enables the client to gain awareness of the levels of tension that are present in the muscles.

In its original form, progressive relaxation was quite elaborate. At one point, Jacobson believed that the client needed to do two one-hour sessions a day for the rest of his or her life. It has been refined into a series of six exercises concerning the arms, feet, chest, forehead, eyes, and speech organs. It begins with basic muscle groups on the dominant side first, and then moves systematically down the body. There are five basic steps: 1) you focus attention on the muscle group; 2) guided by a therapist or tape, the muscle group is tensed; 3) you maintain tension for five to seven seconds (less with the feet); 4) the therapist or audiotape signals when the muscle group is to be released quickly; and 5) you are instructed to continue to passively focus attention on the muscle group as it relaxes, so you can feel the difference between relaxation and tension.

A shorter progressive relaxation procedure may be taught to clients as a home practice exercise, and can also be used to facilitate learning the biofeedback process.

Active progressive relaxation is contraindicated for clients who have hypertension that may be exacerbated by the muscle contractions. Also, certain drugs may be inappropriate when using active progressive relaxation, and a passive progressive relaxation process may be substituted (Figure 11.1). In a passive progressive relaxation exercise, the individual is guided to relax the muscles without the intervening contractions.

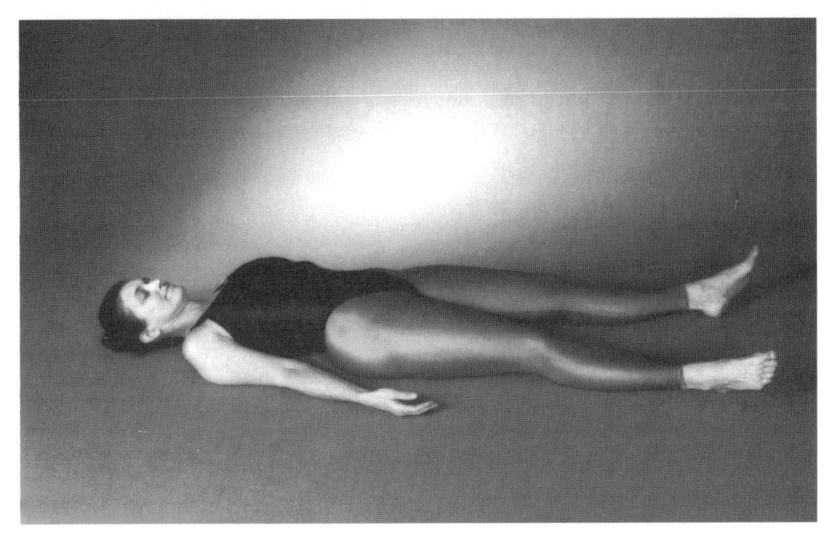

FIGURE 11.1
Relaxation in the corpse or relaxation pose (yoga).

THE RELAXATION RESPONSE

During the 1970s, Herbert Benson was invited with Keith Wallace to participate in research on transcendental meditation (TM). TM was the approach to meditation being taught around the world by the Maharishi Mahesh Yogi and others.

Benson and Wallace designed a study, which has been criticized by many, to look at the psychophysiological effects of meditation. They did not use a control group, nor did they compare the Maharishi's approach with other approaches to meditation. Nevertheless, it was a valuable contribution to meditation research. Their research revealed that oxygen utilization is decreased and heart rate changes occur during transcendental meditation. There were other physiological changes of a similar nature.

Benson later went on to compare this with other forms of relaxation. He determined that a special mantra was not required to achieve the "relaxation response." He gave this term special meaning, and in so doing gave us a great gift. To name something is to give it a handle. We already had a term (from Selye) for the stress response, and a great deal of very valuable research has been done in this area. But we did not have a research concept and strategy for looking at its opposite, the relaxation response.

Benson believed that even a neutral syllable repeated over and over in an appropriate context (a still, quiet environment) would produce the relaxation response, since it would allow for a shift to parasympathetic dominance. Later, Benson went on to say that it did not matter what word or syllable was chosen.

I believe that Benson's original neutral syllable, "one," is especially effective, because in some parts of the world it is the name of God. It is, in addition, a very soothing, complete sound.

Relaxation audiotapes and videotapes have been found to be very useful. The *Relax with Dennis Weaver* videotape, narrated by Eleanor Criswell, is an example of one that we have used extensively and have recorded the physiological data of clients using it at the Biofeedback Training and Research Institute, Cotati, California. The results are consistent with Benson's relaxation response research findings.

YOGA

"No other adjunctive procedure to biofeedback contains so many different methods for developing self-discipline, gaining a sense of inner peace and attaining self-realization. Imagine the benefits of passive exercise, deep breathing techniques, and contemplation that bring about serenity and a sense of well-being."

CYNTHIA LINDWAY, BIOFEEDBACKER

Yoga practices may be used to facilitate learning the biofeedback skill. Yoga is a Sanskrit word, meaning yoke or union. It refers to the unification of the person, body and mind, which is actually a reunification—a remembering of the union which is already there. It is the union of mind and body, person with others, person with the environment, with all of existence.

Yoga was an oral teaching until about 200 B.C., when Patanjali wrote down the oral teachings in the *Yoga Sutras.* The *Yoga Sutras* are aphorisms or elements of a teaching outline.

There are different kinds of yoga. The approaches to yoga that relate most directly to biofeedback training are hatha and raja yoga. Hatha yoga specializes in the physical practices, which include postures, breathing exercises, and progressive relaxation (pratyahara). Raja yoga specializes in meditation and related practices.

One might, when it is indicated, use the eight limbs of raja yoga as an adjunct to biofeedback. These are: 1) the yamas, or things to remember; 2) the niyamas, or things to avoid; 3) postures; 4) breathing exercises; 5) progressive relaxation; 6) concentration; 7) meditation; and 8) unification (Figures 11.2A and 11.2B). These practices would be appropriate when the client expresses an interest in learning more about yoga.

MEDITATION

There are many approaches to meditation from many cultural traditions (Zen, Buddhist traditions, yoga, and many from other religious and non-religious traditions). Meditation generally includes clearing the mind, quieting the body, concentrating on a central focus, and maintaining that mind/body state for a length of time. It usually includes repetition of a stimulus input. The central focus of concentration can be internal or external. External foci can be auditory (for example, chanting mantras), visual (for example, mandala or candle), kinesthetic (for example, slow walking or breathing), and so forth. There is even meditation without an object of central focus or concentration.

With biofeedback, meditation is used as an adjunctive procedure to help foster the desired psychophysiological changes. Biofeedback enhances the precision of the changes. This enhanced precision can be carried into the daily meditation practice and other home practices.

SOMATIC EXERCISES

The Somatic Exercises™ developed by Thomas Hanna are a series of movement patterns that return you to awareness and cortical control of your muscles (Hanna, 1988). They were inspired by his knowledge of and experience with the Awareness Through Movement™ exercises created by Moshe Feldenkrais (Feldenkrais, 1972) and further developed by Hanna.

The Somatic Exercises are designed for special purposes, such as to help you regain control of muscles that are chronically contracted. Chronically contracted muscles create postural imbalances, movement restrictions, and sometimes pain. When muscle contraction levels are balanced—front, back, and sides—we stand up against gravity in a comfortable upright posture. Somatic

FIGURE 11.2A
Meditation in the lotus position.

FIGURE 11.2B
Meditation in the pose of the adept.

Exercises are also used to enhance movement for dancers, athletes, fitness enthusiasts, and so forth.

Somatic Exercises are done slowly, gently, and with awareness. After they are learned, they do not require many repetitions. They are done daily (perhaps twice a day) or when needed. In doing the movement patterns, you voluntarily contract certain muscles or muscle groups and slowly decrease the contractions. (This is not an isometric exercise, because the contractions accompany movements.) Although they are usually done lying or sitting on the floor or table, gravity often serves as the "load" on the muscles being used. After the exercises, the muscles are at a new resting contraction level (and therefore, relaxed). This means that they have a greater number of motor units available for the next use of your muscles.

The Somatic Exercises as well as the Awareness Through Movement exercises are valuable adjuncts to biofeedback training. They facilitate the client's learning of somatic self-regulation skills at a very fundamental level.

CHAPTER TWELVE

MORE ADJUNCTIVE PROCEDURES

"In The Meeting of East and West, *my college master at Yale, F. S. C. Northrup, laid down a turgid argument that East and West would encounter each other on a high philosophical plane, a sort of blue continuum. He was wrong. The East now meets the West on very ordinary ground: right here in the human body."*

T. GEORGE HARRIS

"Biofeedback has provided me with the opportunity to learn more about my body and its particular ways of dealing with stress. When I am hooked up to biofeedback machines and well into a relaxation procedure, I begin to experience my body in a totally different way. This altered sense that occurs in my body has proved to be very relaxing and rewarding. It takes me to a place that I want to go to again and again."

LAURA E. RODDY, BIOFEEDBACKER

SYSTEMATIC DESENSITIZATION

Systematic desensitization was developed by Joseph Wolpe. It includes breaking down anxiety response habits step by step, and begins by teaching the client general relaxation. Jacobson's progressive relaxation may be used at this point, and EMG feedback training and work with other modalities may also be used.

The client is then asked to help develop a hierarchy of least-to-most anxiety producing aspects of the phobic or anxiety producing situation. The original hierarchy can be developed using subjective units of distress (SUDS). Beginning with the first level of the hierarchy, the trainer asks the client to visualize the situation or say the word. When the client reacts with arousal to a stimulus from the hierarchy, he or she is asked to drop back to relaxation again. This process is repeated until the person can entertain the target level on the hierarchy and remain relaxed. Then the person moves on to the next highest level, going systematically up the hierarchy until the top is reached. In some cases, it is appropriate to do in vivo (in life) practice so that the individual generalizes the response to the living situation.

A more generalized desensitization may also be done, using the EDR. When the client reaches a topic that causes an elevation of the EDR, indicating undue arousal, he can pause and explore the topic further with the trainer. Questions may include: What associations does the client have about the topic? What was the client thinking when the EDR feedback indicated arousal? The client needs to have the option of keeping this information to himself or herself. Sometimes random thoughts come through which have an arousing component, and the reaction of the EDR may be significant to the client but need not be discussed with the trainer.

The client and trainer continue to explore the topic and possible alternative conditions or options until the individual is able to discuss the topic with a quiet EDR. This can be used as a means of generalizing the biofeedback learning process to everyday situations or as a deeper analytic process in which past events are explored and new relationships to those events are developed. This is a classical conditioning situation in which the person is establishing a new association—relaxation—with the person, object or situation that previously caused undue arousal.

QUIETING RESPONSE (QR)

The quieting response process was developed by Charles Stroebel in Connecticut at the Institute for Living. Elizabeth Stroebel developed a version for children called Kiddie QR. It is an attractive approach to increasing generalization of relaxation in everyday life, and is particularly useful for certain persons. Stroebel has done a good job of packaging it in a way that makes it easier to teach to particular groups of people.

The quieting response is a series of procedures designed to be done briefly at various times during the day. It begins with a cue and a body check. Then the response, if indicated by the cue that one is experiencing undue arousal, includes saying to oneself "Sparkle smile, sparkle eyes" (smile inwardly with the feeling of social responsiveness); taking a deep, but easy, breath (count to four and then exhale your breath); then imagining a feeling of relaxation going from your jaw to shoulders and neck and down your body and out through your toes.

The first step suggests a parasympathetic response which is facilitated by increased fluid over the surface of the eyes (a PNS response), and also suggests the alpha (relaxed) brain waves that often accompany a smile. The second step involves the suggestion of an alert mind in a relaxed body (a Type A mind in a Type B body).

This procedure is completed in a few seconds, and may be repeated frequently in response to inner or outer cues. For example, symbols (colored paper dots) may be placed on one's watch face, or on objects in one's environment as reminders to do the procedure periodically. Or the procedure can be used regularly after certain environmental interactions, such following a phone conversation.

HOME PRACTICE

It is important that home practice be carried out by the client. Some clients very readily move to apply what they have learned in biofeedback to their everyday lives, while others require a bit more prompting. One of the ways a client can move to include bio home practice exercises is by scheduling them into his or her routine. Another way is to keep a log and check off when the exercise is done and what the results are. For example, the stress level after doing the exercise can be evaluated on a scale of one to ten. One can also reinforce oneself in various ways—by rewarding oneself with a short experience of a favored activity, such as watching a bit of television, talking with a friend, taking a warm bath, or simply thanking oneself.

One might think that doing the home practice following training would be so important after a person had gone to such lengths to learn biofeedback skills that such practice would be automatic, but it isn't. It is surprising how many well-meaning people cannot find time or can't remember to do something so vitally important as home practice. So it may require a little "shaping" of the home practice behavior to bring it into the person's behavioral repertoire.

VISUALIZATION

Visualization in biofeedback can be used in a variety of ways to impact on brain function and, therefore, on body function. Or it can be used to listen to the body for information about particular situations. The first approach creates brain and body states such as relaxation or healing, while the second involves becoming aware of the body's wisdom.

An approach to using imagery to affect body states includes visualizing a relaxing, warming scene, or visualizing changes, such as increased peripheral blood flow, which effect warming. This can be done as a result of verbal suggestion from the biofeedback trainer, video or audio tape, script, or self-suggestions.

Approaches to listening or sensing information from the body can take the form of an inner advisor process or allowing images to present themselves in a sort of active imagination (à la Jung), or painting images of a physiological condition which reveal certain elements such as the presence or absence of a space-occupying lesion or tumor.

The inner advisor process has been popularized by Jose Silva, M. Samuels, N. Samuels, D. Bressler, and others.

Visualization is the use of the mind to create an image separate from input from the environment. It may be verbal, as in visualizing a word, or nonverbal, as in visualizing an image, picture, design, or symbol. Since visualization may be verbal or nonverbal, we may be dealing with the left hemisphere of the brain (the verbal hemisphere) or the right hemisphere (the nonverbal, symbolic hemisphere).

Creative visualization is the use of the visualization process to bring new experiences into one's life. It was popularized by Shakti Gawain (1978). The first step is to select something you would like to have happen (considering that the outcome be beneficial to all). The second step is to see it as having already happened. The third step is to act on the vision. This process opens up the possibility within your own mind that such an event can occur. It makes you more receptive toward the desired event, and therefore, when certain events happen on the way to your goal, you will facilitate them. You will not ignore them or inhibit your response to them. For example, if you are trying to find a partner, you must be open to the possibility of finding a partner. When someone wants to talk to you, you pause and start a conversation. You do not decline the invitation to converse.

It may be the case that you are actually impacting on events. Psi-mediated instrumental response (PMIR) was a concept proposed by Rex Stanford, in which the organism impacts on its environment to foster the best possible outcome for itself. In some cases, a person's attitude may look suspiciously as though it is affecting events. An example might be going for a job interview and finding just the "right" circumstances for a favorable response—being interviewed by the person mostly likely to respond favorably, who just happened to be in the office briefly during his vacation. Synchronistic events sometimes suggest PMIR.

If nothing else, after practicing creative visualization you will be less likely to interfere with events, since you have chosen to be receptive to them and relate to them as if they had already happened.

Several years ago, I had occasion to practice visualization and affirmation in vivo. We were doing some spring skiing and decided to go with a friend up to the top of the mountain. It required several ski lifts to get there. I had not had much success with ski lifts. I had tended to fall off when disembarking. At one time I failed to get off in time and had to climb down. As we neared the top, I thought, "Uh-oh." Then it occurred to me to visualize myself getting off easily and effectively. As I left the chair and glided forward, I was astonished at how easy it was. Skiing is a great example of mind/body integration at work.

Just as we program our biocomputers (brains) with cognitions and attitudes, we use the program with our behaviors. Psychophysiology teaches us how to program our biocomputers for effective functioning.

COGNITION AND COGNITIVE RESTRUCTURING

Cognitions are such an important part of biofeedback. A person's attitudes about his or her behavior and situations play an important part in what he or she will allow to happen or will attempt to achieve. One's attitudes set up neural circuits that may inhibit movements in directions that one may consciously desire. For example, if a person comes in for biofeedback and believes in advance that it won't work, that person will put the brakes on any movement in the desired direction. Such a person will almost never be able to do home practice exercises.

Various cognitive restructuring approaches can be combined with biofeedback. The therapist is trying to teach relaxation approaches to the person doing biofeedback training, and as this occurs the therapist frequently discovers that the person cannot relax before certain ancillary conditions are addressed. These conditions may include lack of assertiveness, lack of ability to manage time, problem solving deficiencies, and negative self-statements (self-talk). Therefore, some techniques that come from cognitive behavior modification are useful.

We will explore some of the ones that can be used with biofeedback. The cognitive approaches in biofeedback we'll discuss include: 1) behavioral rehearsal; 2) cognitive training; 3) cognitive restructuring; 4) the use of models; 5) the use of role playing; 6) role reversal; 7) self-behavioral management; and 8) thought stopping.

BEHAVIORAL REHEARSAL AND BIOFEEDBACK

In behavioral rehearsal, the individual tries on or rehearses the desired behavior. For example, a person anticipating a job interview might rehearse interview behaviors. The biofeedback instrument would show the physiological responses, and the individual would learn how to keep an optimal level of physiological arousal while being interviewed, thus improving performance during the actual interview.

COGNITIVE TRAINING AND BIOFEEDBACK

Cognitive training is helpful when stress responses result from cognitions (thoughts, attitudes, or beliefs). What a client says in the biofeedback interview will reveal the extent that thoughts, attitudes and beliefs contribute to the problem. New insights and cognitions are gained by working through the thoughts, attitudes and beliefs with the aid of biofeedback instrumentation. Some of these new cognitions greatly reduce the stress of the situation. Sometimes the problem is solved. With biofeedback, the individual is able to see how the cognitions contribute to physiological arousal, and can experience how relaxing it is to adopt a new cognition.

Cognitive Restructuring Cognitive restructuring enables the person to substitute positive, self-enhancing or coping thoughts for habitual negative ones (negative self-talk or self-statements). When one is working with a client, it becomes apparent what kind of cognition the client has. One can hear the cognitions he has about himself and others. For example, a client might say that she is "sick" because she has felt this or that. She may say she is "dumb" because she has done this or that. Adding the emotional self-criticism to the behavior does not foster change, but merely adds to the depressive quality of the experience. Therefore, the individual needs to see the effect of her cognitions on her physiological state.

It is amazing how a belief or attitude can alter the significance of an event. This belief will psychophysiologically impact on the person, and the impact can be seen and heard in the way the person expresses himself. Likewise, the effect of substituting coping thoughts for negative ones can be seen in the person's self-expression and biofeedback recordings.

Various cognitive restructuring approaches can be combined. Following the initial training, the client can do the same thing, subvocally, and the process can take place wherever the client may be.

The Use of Models in Biofeedback Modeling uses a person as an example of a skill. It has been said that a Type A personality cannot teach another to be a Type B personality (Type A and Type B personalities refer to the types of individuals who are respectively prone and less prone to coronary attacks, as described by Friedman and Rosenman). Symbolic modeling is achieved through the use of audio, video, films, and computer/compact disks (CDs). Clients can listen to tapes that guide them in relaxation exercises, in which the voices model a soothing state. Videotapes or CDs, for example, can be used for client education, in which the client can learn about his or her condition. The client can also see actors modeling healthy behavior and recovery behavior.

A covert model refers to the client imagining or visualizing the desired behavior. The imagined behavior can occur in guided imagery. It can also occur with behavioral rehearsal using words to describe the ideas.

The Use of Role Playing with Biofeedback Role playing is done in simulated situations in the lab with biofeedback equipment, prior to enacting the desired behavior in the real situation. In role playing, the individual takes the role of someone exhibiting the desired behavior. The role may be of someone in a well state. It may be of someone with whom the individual is dealing. Through role playing the individual gets the chance to experience what it is like to play that role.

You can also rehearse the desired behavior. This enables the person to engage in the desired behavior more easily at the appropriate time. This can be done in a simulated environment, or in the real environment with the appropriate arrangements. For example, when working with a person who has a fear of flying, one can use systematic desensitization to reduce the arousal response, and then the person can practice the relaxation response while in an airplane or airplane simulator.

Role Reversal in Biofeedback Role reversal enables the person to experience the role of another while receiving biofeedback. It is particularly useful in examining the other person's attitudes and beliefs from the inside. For example, I once had a client whose stress was caused by a very angry boss. When the client assumed the role of his boss, he suddenly got an insight into what it was like to be that person. He could feel his boss's anger. He could feel why his boss was angry, and he could recognize that this was his boss's problem—he did not need to identify with his boss's anger. All he needed was to try to understand the basic content of the communication between them.

With role reversal using biofeedback, the individual is monitored with the biofeedback instruments while playing the role. He or she is able to experience the physiological impact of the role evidenced by the instrument readings.

Self-Behavioral Management Self-behavioral management refers to using a system of tracking and monitoring behaviors to enhance learning the biofeedback skills. A simple system of checking off behaviors on a checklist can help the individual make certain behaviors more conscious. This way the person becomes more self-directed, and can transfer the skill of behavioral management into everyday life. The clients administer the strategy, then evaluate the degree to which they have fulfilled their goals. This can be used with home practice schedules, use of skills in everyday situations (generalization), and monitoring desired behaviors.

Thought Stopping and Biofeedback Thought stopping is useful when a person is bothered by a persistent thought that disturbs his functioning. In biofeedback, it can be seen to produce a stress response. When other efforts to stop the obsessive thought have not worked, thought stopping used adjunctively with biofeedback begins with a feedback session. During the session, the client entertains the thought. At that moment the therapist shouts "Stop!" or "Stop, stop, stop!" accompanied by a loud clap. The obtrusive thought is then replaced by a more appropriate thought.

This enables the person to disrupt the neural circuit involved with the thought. He can then encourage another circuit to function. With biofeedback training, the person becomes aware of the impact of the thought on his physiology. He can experience the difference between the unwanted thought and the pleasant one, as demonstrated on the biofeedback instrument. The desired state can be confirmed.

CONCLUSION

In conclusion, there are many methods for facilitating the learning of biofeedback and somatics skills. This chapter has covered some of them. The next chapter will present some of the principles necessary for understanding the stress-relaxation continuum in which we all live.

PART II

Biofeedback, Relaxation, and Performance

CHAPTER THIRTEEN

BIOFEEDBACK, RELAXATION AND STRESS MANAGEMENT

"Stress is the nonspecific response of the body to any demand; the state manifested by the specific syndrome which consists of all the nonspecifically induced changes within a biologic system."

HANS SELYE

"Biofeedback helped me get more in touch with what was going on for me in the here and now. It has helped me to learn what my physiological responses to stress and arousal are and to lessen the negative side-effects that are bad for me. For the first time in my 46 years, I feel I am getting in touch with my body."

SUZIE A. RENO, BIOFEEDBACKER

"It has been researched over a period of years that blacks are at great risk for stress due to their environment, diet and health problems. I really found that my biofeedback sessions benefitted me greatly, teaching me how to relax. I'm a black female and learning to relax in a painless manner made it even more relaxing. I hope to learn about biofeedback and introduce it to the black community."

MEOKIA FRIERSON, BIOFEEDBACKER

Biofeedback and somatics both relate to the stress-relaxation continuum. Biofeedback and somatics responses are altered by stress; they both positively impact on stress levels. Because the stress/relaxation research is considered such a valuable dimension for this work, I have devoted an entire chapter to exploring the basic concepts and how biofeedback and somatics can be used to address relevant issues.

I have become increasingly aware of the importance of stress management training. You need to be clearly aware of the nature of stress and your responses to it. It is important to know how to manage your physiology in order to cope with a variety of life situations. Thus prepared, you will be able to do crisis intervention with yourself and others. The ability to self-regulate provides a baseline of homeostatic balance that is comfortable and healthy.

Stress has been defined by Hans Selye (1974) as "the nonspecific response of the body to any demand; the state manifested by the specific syndrome which consists of all of the nonspecifically-induced stress changes within a biological system." We all experience stress—mild to severe—from time to time. Selye emphasized that stress is important for our physiological well-being and that there are negative effects of stress as well as positive ones. The positive stress he referred to as "eustress."

When we experience a stressor in our environment, we have an initial reaction that is followed by various stages of our response to stress. Selye identified three stages of the stress response, which he called the general adaptation syndrome (GAS) in 1936. The three phases include "l) the alarm reaction; 2) the stage of resistance; and 3) the stage of exhaustion" (Selye, 1974, p. 38). The alarm reaction occurs when "the body shows the changes characteristic of the first exposure to stress" (p. 38). In the resistance stage, resistance of the body decreases. In this stage of resistance, physiological resistance increases. "If a stressor is sufficiently strong (e.g., severe burns, extremes of temperature), death may result" (p. 38).

The second phase, the stage of resistance, "ensues if continued exposure to the stressor is compatible with adaptation. The bodily signs characteristic of the alarm reaction have virtually disappeared, and resistance rises above normal" (p. 38).

The third phase, the stage of exhaustion, occurs as "continued exposure to the same stressor, to which the body had become adjusted, eventually exhausts adaptation energy. The signs of the alarm reaction reappear, but now they are irreversible, and the individual dies" (p. 38).

We all experience the alarm reaction with the onset of a stressor. A shift to the resistance stage occurs within a certain period of time, depending on our unique psychophysiologies. The trick is to decrease stress as soon as possible in the resistance stage. This part is deceptive: In the resistance phase one may not feel stressed. After this phase comes burnout.

Selye felt that we have a finite amount of adaptation energy. Adaptation energy might be defined as all of the body's resources needed to cope with stress.

Sources of stress that may be found in the "climate and environment" include: "social and cultural stressors," "crowding," "sensory deprivation and boredom," "isolation and loneliness," "captivity," "relocation and travel," "urbanization," "catastrophes," "meteorological factors," and "neuropsychological stressors" (Selye, 1975, pp. 381–395).

STRESS PHYSIOLOGY

Hormonal Mediation of Stress Reactions According to Selye (1974, p. 42):

> It is now generally recognized that the emergency discharge of epinephrine (adrenalin) represents only one aspect of the acute phase of the initial alarm reaction to stressors. At least equally important in the maintenance of homeostasis—the body's stability—is the hypothalamus-pituitary-adrenocortical axis, which probably participates in the development of many disease phenomena as well. This "axis" is a coordinated system consisting of the hypothalamus, which is connected with the pituitary gland (hypophysis), and the pituitary gland, which regulates adrenocortical activity. The stressor excites the hypothalamus (through pathways not yet fully identified) to produce a substance that stimulates the anterior pituitary to discharge the hormone ACTH (adrenocorticotrophic hormone) into the blood. ACTH in turn induces the external, cortical portion of the adrenal gland to secrete corticoids. These elicit thymus shrinkage, simultaneously with many other changes such as atrophy of the lymph nodes, inhibition of inflammatory reactions and production of sugar (a readily available source of energy).
>
> Another typical feature of stress reaction is the development of peptic ulcers in the stomach and intestines. Their production is facilitated through an increased level of corticoids in the blood, and the autonomic nervous system plays a role in eliciting ulcers.

Endocrine Gland System Endocrine glands are hormone-producing organs. They include, from your head down, the pituitary, thyroid, adrenals, ovaries, and testes. They secrete hormones directly into your circulatory system. We are indirectly aware of the effect of biofeedback training on the activity of the endocrine glands. For example, the person with an underactive thyroid receiving thyroxin may need less of it while doing biofeedback training. When adrenals relax rather than having a stress response, they may produce less cortisol (cortisol is the primary gluticorticoid hormone secreted by the adrenal gland).

Adrenal Glands The adrenal cortex is located at the outer region of the adrenal gland. It produces adrenocorticosteroids.

The adrenal medulla rests in the inner part of the adrenal gland. It produces epinephrine and norepinephrine. The adrenal medulla secretes its hormones into the circulatory system.

Self-Observable Signs of Stress Hans Selye included the following self-observable signs of stress in his landmark book, *The Stress of Life* (1975, pp. 174–178): "general irritability, hyperexcitation or depression," "pounding of the heart," "dryness of the throat and mouth," "impulsive behavior," "emotional instability," "the overpowering urge to cry or run and hide," "inability to concentrate," "feelings of unreality, weakness or dizziness," tendency to become "fatigued, loss of joie de vivre," "floating anxiety," "emotional tension and alertness, feeling of being 'keyed up,'" "trembling, nervous tics," "tendency to be easily startled by small sounds," "high pitched, nervous laughter," "stuttering and other speech difficulties," "bruxism or grinding of the teeth," "insomnia," "hypermotility . . . hyperkinesis (an increased tendency to move about without any reason)," "sweating," "the frequent need to urinate," "diarrhea, indigestion, queasiness in the stomach, and sometimes even vomiting," "migraine headaches," "premenstrual tension or missed menstrual cycles," "pain in the neck or lower back," "loss of or excessive appetite," "increased smoking, increased use of legally prescribed drugs" ("such as, tranquilizers or amphetamines"), "alcohol or drug addiction," "nightmares," "neurotic behavior," "psychosis," and "accident proneness." And there are others unique to you.

T. H. Holmes and R. H. Rahe developed a scale of "life change units" that rated the stress potential of various aspects of life. They conducted research on different groups of people and correlated their stress scores with later medical and other difficulties. They found that high stress scores correlated with increased health problems and concerns. Since that time, others have developed more elaborate ways of assessing stress. For example, Dennis Jaffe and others developed the ESSE Stress Map. Stress profiles have also been developed, some of which include psychophysiological measures recorded with biofeedback instruments.

STRESS MANAGEMENT

Exercise An important part of stress management is exercise. We are all aware of the importance of cardiovascular health. It has been stated that at least 20 minutes of relatively vigorous exercise daily is essential to maintain cardiovascular health. (The heart is a muscle, we are reminded, and it requires exercise to maintain its healthy functioning.) Happily, recent research indicates that even moderate exercise will enhance health. Moderate exercise is defined as approximately half an hour of vigorous walking per day, done consistently.

Exercise can take a variety of forms: walking, jogging, swimming, aerobics, etc. Strength, flexibility and endurance are important outcomes of exercise. There are also mood enhancing elements of exercises.

The Psychosomatic Client As the work of William Rickles, M.D., and others illustrate, the personality of the client is significant in how training needs to be conducted. Indeed, certain personalities who cannot readily experience any other kind of therapy may benefit from biofeedback therapy.

Personality is the result of temperament and environment (childhood experiences, etc.). It has a physiological and psychological etiology. It especially has an interactive etiology, in that there is a genetic-physiological-psychological interaction. Childhood experiences interact with certain physiological predispositions to release certain elements in the personality makeup.

Personality makeup makes a difference in how treatment/training is designed, and how the biofeedback therapy is conducted (including communication between the client and therapist).

Biofeedback and Relaxation in Psychotherapy for Stress Management Biofeedback training in psychotherapy is done in at least two ways. It may be used as an adjunct to the psychotherapeutic process, enabling the person either to decrease arousal level (anxiety and stress) to a mid-range level where psychological work is possible, or to increase arousal level so that the person is more motivated and connected with life and hope.

Sometimes called biofeedback-assisted psychotherapy, it enables the client and counselor to hear and see the feedback in relationship to arousal around topics that are discussed. This enables them to stop and discuss more fully topics that elicit an increased arousal level. The client discusses associations with the topic and explores new cognitions regarding it.

An important part of stress management is relaxation (see Appendix C). A daily (and ideally twice a day) relaxation period of 15–20 minutes is essential for bringing stress levels down so that the cumulative effects of stress do not continue to climb. Your relaxation training can take a variety of forms, as discussed in Chapters 11 and 12.* Coming back to homeostasis daily assists in fostering parasympathetic nervous system activity, which concerns rest, maintenance, repair, and a sense of well-being.

---

* For information about Stress Management Education certification, contact the Biofeedback Certification Institute of America, 10200 West 44th Avenue, #304, Wheatridge, CO 80033-2840; (303) 422-8436.

CHAPTER FOURTEEN

BIOFEEDBACK IN EDUCATION

"Biofeedback applications to education are only beginning. . . . Many of these processes can be used in groups, with the feedback itself providing the individual instruction needed. Once one takes the cybernetic viewpoint that feedback can help the learning process, anything can be used for feedback: audio- and videotape recordings, immediate verbal feedback from the teacher, etc. The major process that biofeedback learning implies and encourages is learning through passive attention, to grasp without grasping—through which we can allow ourselves to open an infinite world in which to expand our own potentials."

ERIK PEPER

"Stress management should be taught in schools to children as preventative measures for physical and emotional illnesses. I have a long way to go in making this a natural part of my 'being,' but I will practice diligently as I believe in the relationship that stress has with the mind, body, and spirit. It certainly correlates with biofeedback and somatics. Actually, they cannot be separated."

HELEN ELAINE, BIOFEEDBACKER

Carl Rogers wrote about the fully functioning person, Abraham Maslow talked of the self-actualizing person, and Carl Jung talked of the balanced development of the individuated person. We are now in a position to enhance these processes through still another means—biofeedback training.

The central concern of the field of education is the process of learning. Within recent times a new modality for facilitating learning has been successfully developed but has not yet been fully appreciated by educators: this is the modality of biofeedback. Whereas biofeedback has been generally used by physicians, psychologists, and other clinicians, its possible uses are equally vast at all levels of the educational domain—elementary school, high school, college, continuing education programs, and on-the-job training programs. Biofeedback researchers have not made clear the many direct and indirect uses which educators can make of biofeedback, not only for students but for teachers and others as well. This section is an effort to suggest some of the many applications of biofeedback in the learning process.

From a humanistic perspective, biofeedback training can be seen as developing increased self-regulation and self-control for the fulfillment of the person's potential. Holistic development and actualizing potential, self-direction and self-esteem, and first-person perceptions and third-person perceptions are humanistic concepts that are part of the biofeedback training experience.

Whether behavioristic or humanistic, biofeedback can be viewed as a special instance of the Feldenkrais learning concept of Functional Integration Theory (Feldenkrais, 1972). Differentiation of a function (separating the function [such as through EMG feedback] from the combined systems), exercising that function, attention to that function, and integration of the function back into the total organization of the individual comprise Feldenkrais's understanding of how learning and development take place.

Not only does biofeedback seem to improve the functional organization of the individual, but the results sometimes far exceed the training experience itself. The training experience (which is itself valuable) does not explain the speed or scope of some of the behavioral changes.

Perhaps one way of understanding it is in terms of the "learned helplessness" syndrome. Helpless, hopeless, and fatigued, the individual who repeatedly fails in a situation ceases to try to succeed in even the simplest tasks. This person may be placed in a potentially successful situation, but he or she still will be unable to try.

Such helplessness can be learned (Seligman, 1973). One of the ways to break the learned helplessness syndrome is retroactive therapy, which provides small success experiences (minimal responses that are reinforced to shape behavior until it is self-directed). These experiences are steadily increased. At a certain point the individual experiences himself as able; he can control not only his bodily state, but the way the environment impacts on him. He becomes what he previously had been unable to be, and can now generalize that ability to other life decisions.

What actually causes such changes? Biofeedback researchers, as careful, diligent and innovative as they are, have only begun to explore the many levels (molar and molecular) of explanation.

If biofeedback can change behavior, if it can facilitate personal development, if it can increase self-control, then it holds great promise for the field of education. But how? Let us look at how biofeedback has been used by educators, and how it can be used.

On the face of it, biofeedback represents a further extension of the concept of holistic education; it is a form of somatic (mind/body unification) training. In this case it is a new approach—utilizing technological aids—to the holistic education of the individual. Mental, physical and emotional behavior can be facilitated through specific biofeedback training.

There appears to be a lack of communication between biofeedback researchers and practitioners, and professional educators who are committed to facilitating self-exploration, self-regulation and self-awareness. Many researchers, and a few educators, have demonstrated the potential uses of the technology for education. Thomas Mulholland (1973) suggested certain ways in which educators can use biofeedback: 1) as a vehicle to expand awareness and explore the mind, without drugs; 2) as a general method for accentuating processes conducive to learning, and diminishing those that impede learning; and 3) as a way to strengthen specific skills, such as relaxing certain muscles or increasing certain brain rhythms.

The contemporary American educational model defines learning in terms of the information provided. Students, however, have been "tuning in" to their own psychophysiologies through such means as drugs and meditation. The biofeedback model provides an acceptable technological tool for self-exploration, a goal generally shared by both students and educators. Biofeedback uses sophisticated electronic devices to give objective information to the student about his or her body, and the student learns to expand and regulate his or her self-awareness. This approach to education stresses the evaluation of differences in using information, rather than simply measuring how much information is used in learning.

Little is known about the attentional processes that enable a student to learn more efficiently. Much useful information has been obtained at the Naval Academy about how students' study habits, day dreaming and grade levels may be related to their specific EEG patterns. In a study of 50 upcoming graduating students with cumulative grade point averages between 3.5 and 4.0, significant differences in alpha rhythms were found in students with low and high grade point averages. Students with high grade point averages were more relaxed and produced more alpha rhythms, while those with lower grades spent more time worrying. During a test the students with high grades exhibited a span of 180 seconds of alpha at 8–13 Hz; the students with low grade had only 140 seconds of alpha rhythm during the same time. Neurologists studying their EEGs could not detect these differences. "Assuming the groups are otherwise neurologically equal, the high grade point students seem more relaxed, produce more alpha waves and do better in school," commented Dr. Monitor in the *Naval Scientist* (1974).

In another study, EEGs were recorded during rest and during periods of mental effort in two samples of normal young males. Relationships were investigated between EEG slow waves, alpha index, alpha frequency, beta index, beta frequency, and three separate indices of mental ability: 1) general level of mental ability; 2) the Automatization Cognitive style, defined as greater ability (strong automatization) or lesser ability (weaker automatization) to perform simple repetitive tasks than expected from the individual's general level of mental ability; and 3) performance on intellectual tasks while the EEG was being recorded. Principal findings were that slow waves and slow alpha frequencies were positively associated with both automatization ability and with efficient cognitive performance under conditions of mental effort, and that Automatization Cognitive style was inversely related to beta index during periods of mental effort. These results were interpreted as providing evidence of stable and meaningful relationships between mental abilities and neurophysical events as reflected in the EEG (Vogel et al., 1968).

Since an increase in alpha and theta rhythms is associated with day dreaming, inattention to visual stimuli and a decrease in alertness, some biofeedback researchers have hypothesized that students trained to suppress alpha will increase their alertness and comprehension. Whether a specific learning task is best facilitated in a state of relaxed musculature and increased production of alpha brain waves or high arousal and an increase in cortical activity, the student can learn through biofeedback to regulate his or her own level of arousal and attention. The learner will also recognize that emotional state has an effect on the learning process. Anxiety, fear and tension can impede reception, processing and retrieval of information, and the student can come to recognize and maintain those physiological states associated with pleasant feelings while learning. Biofeedback training with students reporting test anxiety and fears having to do with reading is currently being explored.

Paivo (1971) cites evidence that imagery is the most potent predictor of performance in verbal learning. Images and ease of learning are not related in a cause-and-effect manner, but are related because both reflect some fundamental process that, through biofeedback training, becomes accessible to direct conscious experience and is reflected in behavior. When Kamiya and Zeitlan (1963) trained subjects to successfully control their alpha waves, the subjects reported that the self-produced controlling stimulus was some form of visual imagery. Individuals who learn awareness and control of their internal processes also learn to produce and control mental imagery.

Green et al. (1971) hypothesized that through theta and alpha training subjects would enter a state of consciousness particularly conducive to creating thinking. Alpha imagery has been described by subjects as drifting, fantasies, and daydreams (Haight et al., 1974), and with increased theta, a reverie state with hypnagogic-like imagery occurs.

Specific processes that impede learning, such as mental retardation, learning disabilities, hyperkinesia, poor self-concept, and lack of motivation are the subjects of recent biofeedback studies. Kimmel et al. (1977) found that if retarded children were rewarded for producing GSR orienting responses to stimuli of different visual forms, their performances on a later formboard task were improved. By tapping into the physiology of attention, the goal here is to use the feedback training to increase attention and therefore increase transfer of learning.

Considerable attention has been focused in recent years on the rather heterogeneous clinical grouping termed "learning disability." Usually, children with learning disabilities can be characterized by no hard neurological disturbances, no primary sensory or motor defects, no apparent primary emotional disturbances, but with low-normal intelligence quotients. The main presenting problem is that these children are slow to learn; they are either retarded in grade level or are in special classes. Significant decrements were obtained specifically in the 40 Hz EEG band during problem-solving tasks in a carefully selected group of such children. With biofeedback training for 40 Hz EEG with five subjects, there were significant mean increases in 40 Hz responses on the two problem tasks and a rise during both problem-solving periods. All subjects also showed a significant improvement in the number of correct responses on both sets of problems (Sheer, 1975).

Hyperkinesis is a designation applied to a varying set of problems occurring in childhood. The most frequently cited symptoms are overactivity, short attention span and impulsivity, with associated learning disabilities and feelings of failure that produce a negative self-image. Biofeedback for reduction of muscular tension resulted in reduction of muscular tension, hyperactivity, and distractibility and emotionality-aggression (Braud et al., 1975).

Continuation high school students in California are drop-outs from the traditional schools and are characterized as maladjusted, hostile, and anxious, with poor self-concept and learning skills. At the conclusion of biofeedback training, three continuation students reported that learning how tense they were, and that they could do something about it, had a positive influence on them. Teachers reported improvements in motivation, attitudes about school and interpersonal relationships (Haight, 1975). Biofeedback as a tool in the science curriculum in a continuation school has stimulated the inquiry process of the students, since they explore their own nervous systems and become aware of their own individual abilities and talents (King, 1975).

Over the past 24 years Criswell (1970) has been using biofeedback to facilitate the educational process at Sonoma State University on the undergraduate and graduate level (Figure 14.1). There has been a biofeedback lab in the Psychology Department since 1969. Professors, staff, community members, and students have used it in several ways—for individual projects, for personal exploration, for individual problem solving, and to evaluate learning (such as the effects of learning yoga or zen meditation or athletics). It has been used as an aid in the learning of concepts in courses such as physiological psychology, learning, and perception, and as a research tool in courses such as statistics and experimental design. In response to a survey of student interests, the Biofeedback and Consciousness course was established. For approximately eight years, Biofeedback and Consciousness Research (Criswell), Biofeedback Practicum (co-taught with Stephen E. Wall), and the Biofeedback Internship (co-taught with Stephen E. Wall) have been offered. These courses make up the professional training sequence and extend over a period of a year and a half. The intern and practicum students provide biofeedback training for Sonoma State University students, faculty, staff, and selected community members. The program has become a flexible adjunct to the educational process.

After having looked at some of the ways biofeedback has been used, let us now look at some of the ways it can be used—the future of biofeedback in education.

What are the many educational areas where application is possible? Since biofeedback is a multipurpose discipline, the client—administrator, teacher or student—can use it to facilitate his or her daily tasks, promote teaching/

Media Services, Sonoma State University

FIGURE 14.1
Biofeedback demonstration of graphing capabilities in the Psychology 454 Biofeedback and Somatic Psychology class at Sonoma State University by students Elizabeth Boles and Donna Jenkins.

learning, and evaluate the learning of skills or concepts. It is versatile, and can be used for special problems, general learning, or overall development of the person.

BIOFEEDBACK FOR THE TEACHER

Just as professional teachers need to be alert and effective in the classroom, they also need to be able to relax when the work day is over. Stressful education jobs require that one learn to relax in order to retard fatigue and have maximum healthful sleep. But how? The job uses an enormous amount of energy; each moment of the day has its pressures and demands, and very little of the structure of the day encourages relaxation. How teachers can relax, recuperate, and rest is a matter of prime concern. Biofeedback training can enable the teacher to establish an always-controllable level of relaxation that reduces fatigue.

The teacher who is relaxed, refreshed, and calm will be able to provide a classroom atmosphere that does not encourage the tension and anxiety that frequently accompany learning. This kind of atmosphere leads to good classroom management (discipline).

When teachers have a better tension/relaxation balance on the job, when they can relax more quickly at the end of the day, when they can sleep more easily (more deeply and for longer periods), then they will teach in the most effective manner possible, with flexibility, alertness and good humor. Biofeedback training can aid that balance.

BIOFEEDBACK FOR THE STUDENT

Relaxation training, increasing concentration and attention, and recognizing the validity of one's own learning strategies through biofeedback can enhance the learning experience. From biofeedback's effect on the self-concept of the learner will come increases in self-understanding, self-esteem, self-control, self-direction, and an understanding of the person's own way of dealing with situations.

Facilitating the learning process entails biofeedback training to achieve the optimal level of alertness (activation/arousal) for a particular task or learning experience, and learning what state of relaxation facilitates remembering, how to motivate oneself, how anxiety and tension interfere with effective learning, and how emotional states accompany levels of excitation. One's relationship to each of these dimensions is highly individual, highly dependent on one's physiological/psychological state in the moment and one's ability to self-regulate that state. Psychophysical monitoring and biofeedback training, autogenic training and progressive relaxation, guided imagery and desensitization can all maximize the individual's ability to relate effectively to the learning experience.

Research in hemispheric specialization has confirmed one important insight: Creative intelligence is different from general intelligence (Ornstein, 1972). If we treat these findings metaphorically, logical, linear thinking is more a function of the left hemisphere of the brain; creative, nonlinear thinking is more a function of the right hemisphere. Because we can monitor and feed back the activity of each hemisphere separately or measure synchronization of the hemispheres, biofeedback can be used to enhance creativity and problem solving through maximizing the psychophysiological balance required for each activity.

Biofeedback training will enable us to interface with new educational technology, i.e., other systems that will further enhance learning: Computer-assisted instruction, video, interactive video, computerized information processing systems, virtual reality simulations, telecommunications, video games, electronic calculators. These are examples of the biofeedback and psychophysical monitored combinations that are evolving to expand the educational experience.

Biofeedback will be used creatively to teach human psychology, physiology, neuroanatomy, electronics and general science. The student will be his own laboratory subject and do experiments on himself and others. The learning process will be internally directed and the student will create/reinforce a belief system concerning the control he has over himself and his environment. He will become a more active participant in his education.

BIOFEEDBACK IN THE EMOTIONAL DOMAIN

The guidance counselor or school psychologist (if he or she is a trained biofeedback therapist) will work with stuttering, school phobia, test anxiety, interpersonal difficulties, hyperkinesis, and other problems which may have physiological correlates. The special education teacher will use biofeedback to aid in diagnosis and individualization of appropriate procedures. Physical educators will use biofeedback as an aid to understanding the emotional/motivational component of athletic performance.

BIOFEEDBACK IN THE PHYSICAL HEALTH DOMAIN

The school nurse and school physician who are specially trained in biofeedback therapy will deal with a number of problems, using not only biofeedback but other somatic therapies. Biofeedback will be used with asthma, essential hypertension, chronic muscle tension, migraine headaches, chronic muscle contraction headaches, and other psychophysical complaints, depending on the family, school, and community resources and needs. Various school personnel—classroom teachers, school nurses and counselors, biofeedback consultants—will provide biofeedback in a variety of settings within the school system and by referral to outside agencies.

Biofeedback, a most adaptable tool, can be used in all phases of the educational process. The evolution of holistic education will be furthered through the use of biofeedback by innovative teachers, students, and other school personnel. We believe that educators will increasingly incorporate the findings of biofeedback research and applications into the educational process. We seem to be cresting into an era in which education can be more complete than ever before: fully functioning, fully integrated, actualizing individuals will be the outcome of this more holistic process.

This chapter was based on an article that appeared in the first edition of *Somatics: The Magazine/Journal of the Bodily Arts and Sciences* (1976). The article was titled "The Future of Biofeedback in Education" and was written by Eleanor Criswell and Maryellen Haight. Although there has been progress in the research and application of biofeedback and adjunctive procedures to the educational process, its great potential for facilitating education and maximum development has yet to be realized. Psychophysiological self-regulation skills should be a part of the educational system from the very beginning. One very necessary addition to the application of biofeedback in educational settings is more research correlating biofeedback training with enhanced educational outcomes. The future of biofeedback in education remains filled with excitement and promise.

CHAPTER FIFTEEN

APPLIED BIOFEEDBACK: THE BUSINESS SETTING

"What will be the effects of educating human beings as optimally adaptive somas? An obvious effect will be that we will have produced incorrigibly healthy human beings. . . .

"But the most explosive effect of somatic education for mutational culture is that it is a releasor of human energy. Energy and power have always been the most profoundly fascinating and desired possessions of the human creature."

THOMAS HANNA

"This semester my experience with biofeedback has given me a tremendous awareness of my own stress level. I can't ignore it any longer. The minute my shoulders start inching their way up toward my ears, I stop myself and utilize one of the many relaxation techniques we've learned. I feel that this simple technique will add years to my life!"

JILL TERRY, BIOFEEDBACKER

Biofeedback training in the business setting follows the same general outline as clinical biofeedback training. The practitioner does a needs assessment regarding the particular environmental context of the work, then conducts a rather generic training regarding biofeedback and stress management. This is more effective when it is connected with the actual stimulus properties of the situation.

In the business setting the general issue of stress reduction is important. Most jobs involve various pressures, including deadlines, responsibilities, risks, and interpersonal interactions.

Each individual responds to these pressures in a characteristic way. Generally, the response is only a fair match for the demands of the situation. There is a great deal of room for teaching the person to achieve a better match, which will result in decreasing unnecessary energy expenditure, less fatigue and wear and tear on the physiology, and an increase in perceptual accuracy, effective decision making, creativity, interpersonal ease, job satisfaction, and pleasure at work.

Some businesses have hired stress reduction and burnout consultants. Employee assistance programs have been developed to help with the process. The number of stress complaints filed as Worker's Compensation cases has increased dramatically in recent years. Stress and burnout have led to such problems as attrition in the workforce, excessive absences, and loss of effective executives due to alcoholism and other drug use (a great deal of time and money is involved in finding, hiring and training replacements for top executives). On the positive side is the need to get maximum performance from employees, which can be served by reducing on-the-job stress.

Biofeedback training can be used for on-the-job skills training, by showing people how to cultivate the most effective learning mode for the desired skill. It is important to develop baselines for effective functioning for each task, and to help the person move toward those states. Job analysis coupled with psychophysiological recording would be helpful here, followed by actual feedback on approximations of the criterion tasks.

For the employee, benefits include relaxation for better handling of the stress and fatigue involved in doing the job. Concentration training would lead to less non-productive time, through more precise organization of the psychophysiology required by the task. There would also be a concomitant increase in self-esteem and self-direction. One of the great difficulties involved in the workforce is motivation, and biofeedback could be useful in increasing employee motivation by increasing job satisfaction and improving the employee's self-concept.

The use of biofeedback training in the workplace is concerned with remedial and preventive training. Presently, there is more financial support (through insurance) for the rehabilitation of injured employees than there is for prevention of injury, although there are some programs devoted to preventive training. Preventive training refers to training programs designed to give the employees knowledge and skills that will keep them functioning in a way that is less likely to cause injury. Such courses/training include stress management, body mechanics, perhaps even psychophysiological awareness and self-regulation, etc. Accidents often happen to the person who is stressed, whose skeletomuscular system is chronically contracted to cope with the stress. When there is a sudden change in the environment, that person is much more likely to respond to it in a way that injures him.

Sometimes biofeedback and somatics are used with injured workers in rehabilitation and for possible return to the workplace in the same job (sometimes with the work setting redesigned or the person trained to work in the setting differently) or a different job within the same company. Sometimes rehabilitation requires training or retraining for another job. Sometimes this is a blessing, but it would be far better not to be injured in the first place.

In creating a biofeedback training program for businesses, it is important to begin with a needs assessment. This requires a visit to the worksite, so the trainer can get a sense of the mission of the company and the subgroup with which he or she is concerned. The trainer needs to observe the employees as they work in the job environment, and interview target employees.

It is very important that confidentiality be followed, and that all group needs are considered. The trainer's principal client is the group for which he or she is providing the training.

The majority of the population is employed in the labor workforce, and a huge number of the waking hours of these people is spent at work. Often, their identities are tied up closely with their careers/vocations. Therefore, it is very important for their quality of life to have healthful, satisfying ways of coping with the stress they experience at work.

In addition, workers also experience career and life transitions, and have networks of family and friends which must also be healthy and satisfying if they are to lead healthy lives. Adults function with maximum health and well-being when they are maximally knowledgeable and able to self-regulate for personal growth and a comfortable sense of themselves within larger systems.

BURNOUT

Burnout is a special topic in business applications of biofeedback training. It also applies to any repeated activity, including the activities of daily living (e.g., child care, leisure time activities). Burnout can be avoided with biofeedback and stress management training and a balanced lifestyle.

STRESS MANAGEMENT FOR PILOTS

Stress management for pilots is another application area of psychophysiological training. It is concerned with teaching pilots about the stressors in their lives and how to manage the stress. It teaches them about how their bodies respond to stress, and how to lower or increase psychophysiological activity levels, depending on the task at hand. One of the first programs to train pilots in this way was developed by Mike Currieri in association with Eleanor Criswell-Hanna.

The Stress Management Awareness Training for Aviators (SMATA) program was designed to train individual pilots as well as small and large groups. The larger the group, the less psychophysiological training depends on biofeedback instrumentation. In such groups, more guided exercises are used to coach the pilots to increase or lower psychophysiological activity levels.

The personality type of people who become pilots has been described as that of a cautious risk taker. Good pilots have been found to be above average in intelligence, to have good spatial reasoning and mechanical ability, to be able to prioritize tasks and to be able to shift priorities flexibly as the need arises.

But in high-stress situations, pilots (like everyone else) may tend to adopt an inflexible focus that is part of the defensive response. The defensive response occurs when the organism defines the situation as life threatening, perhaps including physical annihilation. The defensive response is characterized by flow of blood away from the brain, reduction in sensory sensitivity, increase in heart rate, and a turning away from the stimulus. Stress management training can decrease the likelihood that a crisis will be defined as life threatening, which triggers the defensive reaction.

One of the application areas has to do with psychophysiological training for pilots. Pilots in training currently need to be able to "get up to speed" more rapidly than they have historically needed to do. Until recently, pilots became pilots by learning to fly either privately or in the military, then moving up in the overall system to greater and greater levels of responsibility. Now, however, there is an increased demand for pilots (40,000 will be needed within the next few years), and potential pilots will need to be prepared with a much more direct career path. This means that they will need to "get up to speed" without the benefit of the usual real-time flight experience. Through biofeedback, pilots in training can go through the necessary psychophysiological training experiences more rapidly and cost effectively than they can through putting in hours of actual flight experience without the use of biofeedback.

Biofeedback for pilots is an example of the psychophysiological training of other professionals such as law enforcement officers, fire fighters, rescue workers, emergency medical care providers, military personnel, etc.

BIOFEEDBACK AND LIFE SKILLS

Biofeedback can serve to facilitate every aspect of coping with the life course. It can be used at all developmental stages, such as in childhood coping with the stress of Erik Erickson's "industry versus inferiority" stage, in which self-esteem, self-efficacy and self-concept are so important. In adolescence, it can help with the developmental task of identity clarification. In early adulthood, it can help in learning skills to facilitate the development of intimacy. In middle adulthood, it can help with sorting through generativity issues, including the development of parenting skills and maintaining a sense of autonomy.

In later adulthood and beyond, it can be used to process the "ego integrity versus despair" issue, for example, tuning in on the self separate from the roles (work, family, and the like) that have been used for self-definition in earlier stages. It can also be used to process attitudes about and preparation for the final developmental stage, death.

BIOFEEDBACK AND THE TAO

Biofeedback draws attention to the body's response to various situations. Sometimes the person needs only to listen to this response; at other times, he or she needs to regulate it in order to avoid ill health. Or perhaps the situation itself needs to be changed. Both possibilities need to be open for maximum well-being.

When you are orchestrating your life, you need both to be aware of what you want in order to make it happen, and to be able to allow whatever happens to happen, in accordance with the Tao. The Tao is a Chinese concept (in Chinese, Tao means path) that refers to the flow of events, the balance of factors and forces in the environment—the universe. Sometimes it is appropriate to act to redirect events, while at other times it is important to go with the natural flow, to be in harmony with the way things and events are happening. Biofeedback is a means by which we can choose the most appropriate response to whatever is happening in our lives.

This is true whether we are engaged in work activities or in activities of daily living. The next chapter will explore biofeedback and somatics used for enhanced performance, especially in the arts and athletics.

CHAPTER SIXTEEN

APPLIED BIOFEEDBACK: OPTIMAL PERFORMANCE, ATHLETICS AND THE ARTS

"Western athletes, then, like practitioners of martial arts, often depend on relaxation concentration, breathing exercises, mental emptying, and rhythm to achieve exceptional performances. Even though they don't have a training system as sophisticated in this regard as yoga or the martial arts, they manage nevertheless to incorporate these elements into their practice and performance. Through intrinsic energy or in concert with it athletes often discover extraordinary capacities for strength, speed, balance, and ease."

MICHAEL MURPHY & RHEA A. WHITE

"But perhaps I have worked this metaphor enough to illuminate my central suggestion, namely that creative practices draw upon our entire organism, sensitively guiding its various processes toward new efficiencies, enhancing contact among them, bringing them into resonance with metanormal activities. To do this, our practices must promote perceptual, kinesthetic, communication, and movement abilities; vitality; cognition; volition; command of pain and pleasure; love; and bodily structures."

MICHAEL MURPHY

"I am not an actor or a musician, but I believe that this law still applies to me [the Yerkes-Dodson law, which is the idea that there is an 'inverted-U' that describes performance. One's arousal level rises with one's performance, until one achieves peak performance. Then, as arousal continues, performance begins to decrease.] Writing for me causes arousal.

Often at some point the arousal turns into anxiety. I am guessing that at this point I am on the right side of the inverted-U, because as my anxiety increases, writing becomes more difficult. Through biofeedback I have been learning to recognize the oncoming anxiety and to decrease it through relaxation. By doing so I am further extending my peak performance time."

HALIMAH MCLAUGHLIN, BIOFEEDBACKER

Biofeedback and somatics are very valuable for regaining and maintaining psychophysiological health, but that is not the end of the story. They are also valuable in the enhancement of performance. Biofeedback and somatics are not just devoted to symptom removal. Education for prevention allows us to avoid the symptoms in the first place. There is more to life than symptom removal. The real question is, how does it enhance life? This chapter will explore biofeedback and somatics used to enhance performance.

FACILITATED SKILLED PERFORMANCE

Biofeedback can be applied to various areas of human endeavor. Whenever one needs to manage one's physiology more effectively, biofeedback can aid in that process.

Why would one need to manage one's physiology more effectively? Learning how to manage one's physiology is often a chance matter. People receive some direction in what to do with their bodies as they grow up, but most of the patterns they use are chance combinations of behaviors learned to achieve certain goals. Nevertheless, they do the best they can to utilize their body systems for the tasks at hand.

The application of psychophysiological training to the arts is similar to its application to other specialized human endeavors. The arts often include some instruction in how to use the body, such as breath control in singing, body movements in acting, etc. The kind of instruction varies, and utilization of the rest of the body may not be addressed. Therefore, people wind up doing what they do the best way that they can, often overriding intense fear responses, pain, discomfort, or psychophysiological illness. Some of them have been moved to learn their art as a response to disability and chronic pain.

Biofeedback and related practices can teach the artist the best use of the integrated mind/body, so that some of these problems will not arise or will be self-regulated. Biofeedback and somatics can enhance the art performance and perhaps the end product.

I first became aware of the possibilities through the work of Joan Johnson, who did her doctoral dissertation through Union Graduate School on the effect of biofeedback and somatic exercises on musicianship and creativity. She worked with selected musicians with biofeedback and adjunctive procedures. Videotapes recorded before and after training showed a difference in performance that was subtle but perceivable.

It is also exciting to consider how biofeedback training might affect musicians, many of whom are now suffering and playing that suffering out to the world. What would it be like if they were playing to us from a more integrated mind/body state, characterized by comfort and pleasure rather than pain?

BIOFEEDBACK FOR THE ACTOR

The entire mind/body is the instrument of the actor. Biofeedback for the actor or other performer would mean that in addition to the practice in which he or she must engage in order to tune the bodily instrument, a finer training of the psychophysiology would also be required. Some actors are already quite adept at psychophysiological self-regulation, but others still retain considerable performance anxiety that manifests itself in all of the stress responses. Some actors override the discomfort with a "show must go on" attitude, or they may engage in substance abuse or other self-medication. Recently, a number of actors and other performers have resorted to beta-blockers to reduce the psychophysiological symptoms of performance anxiety. Yet because all medications have varying degrees of side effects, wholesale use of beta-blockers is not a solution.

Through psychophysiological training, performers can learn to distinguish the changes necessary for skilled performance from the learned anxiety responses that seem automatically to accompany the process. The end result would be an improved organization of the psychophysiology for behavioral expression, projection of inner conviction, and verbal communication. It might even contribute to expanding the range of the actor or performer.

Psychophysiological training can facilitate skilled performance in the arts in the following ways: increased psychophysiological comfort and effective utilization of the mind/body; increased awareness of how the body is utilized in the artistic endeavor; awareness of good body mechanics while working;

decreased fatigue; decreased dysponesis in the endeavor; increased insights in the artistic aspects of the endeavor; enhanced creativity; greater interrelation of elements in the situation; and expanded communication of the work (e.g., there are many aspects of a successful artistic career, including how well one can sense opportunities, and how well one can communicate with others not directly involved, such as managers, brokers, agents, customers, family, and friends).

Full artistic expression is only possible if an actor enjoys good health, and the actor's health status determines the length of the career. Biofeedback training can enhance health, prolong life, and thus allow for fuller expression of the actor's vision. This is also true for the dancer and the visual artist.

BIOFEEDBACK IN SKILLED PERFORMANCE

Biofeedback training can be useful for a variety of skilled performances, including sports, piloting, and the arts. Biofeedback used to enhance performance has a different goal than other biofeedback applications, which usually have symptom removal as their direct or indirect goal.

In the area of enhanced performance, the goal is to teach the individual to regulate psychophysiological levels of activity, and then match his or her psychophysiology to the task at hand. For example, the Yerkes-Dodson law indicates that with increased arousal there is an optimal fit between the arousal level and the task at hand. This might be expanded to say that there is also an optimal organization of the organism, perhaps represented by hemispheric dominance, for the task at hand.

PEAK PERFORMANCE

Peak performance is not just for athletes or astronauts. It is for everyone, for you and me. It can be part of everyday life. To look at peak performance, I would like to address the following questions: What is peak performance? Who experiences peak performance? Where is it found? When is it used? Why achieve it? How do we achieve it?

Peak performance is a term popularized by Charles Garfield to refer to the achievement of high levels of performance beyond what is ordinarily available to the person. It is reminiscent of the concept of peak experience described by Abraham Maslow. Peak experiences are those experiences that happen periodically to people in which they are transported beyond their ordinary experiences of life, and in which they experience greater than ordinary levels of insight and effectiveness. They are reported by athletes and by many others.

The concept of optimal performance is useful here. Optimal performance refers to functioning at the most effective and efficient levels, those most appropriate to the task at hand. This is a state for which a person can train through biofeedback and somatics.

INVERTED-U

The inverted-U refers to a graphed comparison of levels of arousal and levels of performance. It was developed originally by Yerkes and Dodson and has been called the Yerkes-Dodson law. Simply, it states that as levels of arousal (excitation, anxiety, etc.) go up, performance increases until it reaches a peak of effectiveness. After this highest level is reached, performance goes down because of a number of factors. Effective performance is a result of a number of factors, including alertness, rhythm of movement, capacity to think through necessary behaviors, and carefulness. I recently had an opportunity to watch this closely while checking into a hotel. The clerk, as nice as he was, was in some state of excitation, moving so rapidly in his tasks that he was making mistakes. His performance had declined.

Simple tasks can be executed at a higher level of excitement than more fine-grained, complex tasks. Hypothetically, there is an optimal level of arousal for every task. As we discussed earlier, we are all trying to match our arousal levels to the task at hand, and we are often trying to strike a balance between decreasing motivation and increasing burnout. Our capacity to match arousal levels with performance can be enhanced through training in self-regulation. Biofeedback is very useful in this process, and there are other approaches as well.

Who experiences peak performance? There has been considerable research conducted with athletes, in business and industrial settings, and in crisis intervention situations regarding peak performance. There are accounts of peak performances by ordinary citizens in emergency situations. We all have the capacity to experience peak performance.

When is it used? Optimal performance becomes relevant when productivity goals are proposed, emergencies or everyday survival situations occur, or ongoing, inner strategies are being developed. In business and health care situations, there has been a recent trend toward measuring productivity in some fashion, collecting data in some way, and communicating the summarized data to the person and the system in which the person works. For example, a hospital or treatment program may tally the number of clients seen, and conduct a discussion of expected productivity levels and the need to increase current levels by various means. In business, increased quotas (of sales, items handled, or items produced) may be related to business practices; in life, it may also be possible to measure productivity and performance in some way. Compensation may be tied to productivity levels; for example, bonus or incentive plans may be instituted in the business environment, in effect putting the person on a reinforcement schedule, as seen from a Skinnerian perspective.

Both persons and pigeons tend to work rapidly for quantitative reinforcers, and when reinforcement is based on increasing levels of output, the person or pigeon can work to the point of exhaustion or burnout. Often, people do not realize that they are working to the point of stress-related concerns or illnesses. Unions have been somewhat helpful in protecting employees from responding to this kind of reinforcement schedule to their detriment, but it is still important to be conscious of and to keep track of quality and quantity of performance required by the job.

Why achieve peak performance? Why not? We should all strive for peak performances, because to do so is more interesting and fun; it adds internal challenges and furthers personal development and individuation. We humans need new stimulation or stimulus changes. We need these just as we need food. If the environment does not provide new, positive stimulation, a person will create it in a negative way. To offset this tendency, it is better to provide it positively.

With appropriate change in stimulation comes pleasure. By definition, interest is peaked by new stimuli, which change the meaning of the situation a bit. New stimuli also increase a person's sense of self-efficacy and self-esteem. We feel good about ourselves when we use ourselves fully and appropriately in a given situation.

Peak performance keeps our physiological systems toned up. Health and integration of our physical systems require that we use them. Aiming toward peak performance has a conditioning effect, and such utilization of our physiological systems will enable us to remain fully functioning in these systems.

Various studies have highlighted the need for us to relate to situations as challenges. Internal challenges are ones in which we set goals and move toward achieving them from the perspective of our inner evaluation and decision making. This has a very tonic effect on the development of our personal potential—physical, emotional, cognitive, behavioral, etc. Later in life this begins to relate to individuation, the process of fulfilling the latent aspects of oneself. The seeds of this are planted in earlier experiences and come more into focus in the later stages of life.

In conclusion, each of us is a world-class athlete in the most significant athletic event—our lives. This way of conceptualizing one's life may enable one to give it the attention that it needs and warrants. Peak performance is not just for special persons or situations. It is for all of us. It is for life.

Dorcas Susan Butt (1987) included the following techniques in her book on sports psychology. This is a valuable list, whether you are an athlete trying to enhance performance, a pilot trying to be safe and productive, or an ordinary citizen trying to live healthily and with a maximum feeling of well-being. The precursors to the use of these approaches in athletics are hypnosis and suggestion.

The techniques included in Butt's list are: "positive thinking" (affirmations) originally popularized by Couè and refined by Dale Carnegie, Aaron Beck and Albert Ellis in cognitive restructuring of negative self-talk; "competence training" through increasing self-esteem and self-confidence with success feedback from the environment versus intrinsic feedback (utilizing the concept of self-efficacy from A. Bandura and J. B. Rotter, including the notion of internal and external locus of control); "meditation," with research support from Herbert Benson, leading to freedom and inner peace; relaxation training and progressive relaxation; "affective control" (using insight from the Yerkes-Dodson law); and "cognitive behavioral" techniques.

"Autogenic training and biofeedback" have been used to train for peak performance (Schultz and Luthe, 1969). "Visual motor behavior rehearsal" starts with general relaxation training and then uses mental imagery to rehearse the desired athletic performance (Suinn, 1980). "Attention control training" uses relaxation training, mental rehearsal and discussion (Nideffer, 1976); "religious and spiritual exploration" involves turning to a power outside oneself for motivation, expectancy, and positive outcome. These are some approaches to facilitating athletic performance that have been used. They can be adapted to any skilled endeavor (Butt, 1987).

How do we achieve peak performance? What are the general principles? Approaches to achieving peak performance include building all systems—mental, physical, emotional and spiritual—to optimal levels of development (we can transcend our limitations/inhibitions) and maintaining developmental levels and integration of systems (exercise/practice, nutrition and new input). We need to achieve and maintain wellness as a baseline, and to continue the refinement of functions in the different systems, differentiating and integrating into new levels of complexity of organization.

To achieve peak performance reliably (or even infrequently) requires that we provide developmental experiences in each system—mental, physical, emotional, and spiritual. We must begin to provide experiences beyond those that are automatically provided by the environment. For example, the environment will require us to develop our cognitive capacity to a certain point in order to survive. We will be educated, in general and specific ways, up to the level required for certain societally supported tasks, such as our jobs. We will need to provide additional experiences if we wish to go beyond this level. Physical development will be encouraged to a certain point during the early part of our lives through adolescence and early adulthood, but to go beyond this (as many people are choosing to do) requires us to become self-directed and to provide the additional training and challenges (such as competition with self or others) that such development requires.

Our limitations are self-imposed. If we think we can only do so much of a task, with practice we will find that we can transcend our limitations over and over again.

GOALS AND OPTIMAL PERFORMANCE

In order to achieve peak or optimal performance, one can think in Timothy Leary's terms of programming the biocomputer (the brain). The brain structure itself is the hardware; the behavioral patterns are in place via learning or the software programming. Goals can be set and visualization used to prepare a person for achieving those goals. Preparation for achieving goals can include learning appropriate behaviors and practice. Ongoing assessment and problem solving can help one know where one is relative to the goals, and how to maximize efforts. One begins with a baseline recording of current states and related behavior. Then one assesses one's level, develops a training plan, logs results, evaluates after the plan has been implemented, and repeats the sequence if the goals have not been achieved.

A balance between proactive and reactive goal setting is desirable. Reactive goal setting is the result of situations and experiences with which one needs to cope, to which one must respond. Proactive goal setting refers to assessing the situation and deliberately setting goals while projecting possibilities that have not yet been realized.

It is valuable to know your life developmental stage. With an awareness of your developmental stage and the developmental tasks that are appropriate for it, you can use the motivation and mobilization of energy in a way that maximizes the effect. You can tie in the desired behavior with the activities relevant to that stage of life. For example, if you are in the generative stage (as described by Erickson), you may piggyback learning some important skills with the child-rearing tasks that are age-appropriate. To an extent, you will do this anyway, but the process can be enhanced through deliberate goal setting. Deliberate goal setting is the key to self-regulation.

Biofeedback and somatics both emphasize self-regulation. With knowledge and awareness, you can use these principles to enhance your life and the lives of others. May you live your life to the fullest, with maximum somatic development and well-being for yourself, others, and the environment.

Biofeedback and somatics are still in their infancies. With the technological revolution that is occurring and the development of the field of biofeedback, it becomes more and more apparent that there are exciting possibilities for the deliberate development of enhanced human function. It also becomes increasingly apparent that this must be done in a balanced manner within the global society for human and environmental health. Each of us must make his or her contribution to the overall well-being of our global environment. Best wishes to you in your life journey and personal evolution.

APPENDIX A

INTRODUCTION TO NEUROANATOMY AND NEUROPHYSIOLOGY FOR BIOFEEDBACK AND SOMATICS

An understanding of neuroanatomy and neurophysiology is valuable in the practice and experiencing of biofeedback and somatics. This appendix presents a number of concepts that are relevant to the understanding and effective practice of biofeedback and somatics. Although the experience of biofeedback and somatics is highly effective without this level of understanding, the entire experience is enhanced by deepening your understanding of what is happening. Our understanding through research and experience continues to deepen and expand. The information we will explore will be changing over time as new insights are gathered. Use this information as a starting point and continue to deepen your knowledge through other sources and continuing education courses and activities.

It is very important to consider the neuroanatomy and neurophysiology of the biofeedback process. Biofeedback is an experience of the relation of mind and body. The process happens because of that link. Therefore, we must remember that there are psychophysiological mechanisms that are behind the effects of biofeedback. We will be more effective in training and learning to the degree that we know how biofeedback works psychophysiologically and use that knowledge to plan appropriate intervention protocols.

When doing biofeedback training, it is important to know what you are doing from a physiological perspective. It is necessary to be able to explain the functions to your client in a relatively comprehensive way. For some clients—less physiologically sophisticated—it may be necessary to explain in greater detail. Some clients may require very simple explanations, pictures, and analogies. You will need to gear your explanation to your client.

You also need to understand the psychophysiology of biofeedback so that you can be maximally successful with your suggestions and interventions. To enable you to understand it at an initial level, the following section will go through the relevant areas.

The entire nervous system of the human being includes several subsystems. The central nervous system (CNS) includes the brain and spinal cord. Outside of the central nervous system is the peripheral nervous system. The peripheral nervous system is divided into two branches: the autonomic nervous system (ANS) and somatic nervous system or skeletomuscular system. The autonomic nervous system is divided into two branches: the sympathetic nervous system (SNS) and the parasympathetic nervous system (PNS).

Nerve impulses are transmitted in the form of action potentials. From sodium-potassium waves transmitted down the neuron comes the depolarization which forms the action potential. At the synapse—the gap between neurons—there is the secretion of a neurotransmitter or transmitter (outside the CNS) substance. It spreads to impact on the postsynaptic membrane of the next neuron. If the impact on the next neuron is sufficient, then an action potential will result from the depolarization of the membrane of the cell. The action potential is conducted down the neuron in an all-or-none fashion aided by the myelin sheath which surrounds the axon.

In doing biofeedback training, it is important to remember that the human may be considered a system of physiological systems. The biofeedback modalities chiefly record the electrical changes or byproducts of these changes—EMG (the electromyograph) measures muscle electrical activity, and EEG (the electroencephalograph) measures brain electrical activity; ST (skin temperature) is measuring the change in blood flow to the extremities; and EDA (electrodermal activity) is looking at the flow of an electrical current across the surface of the skin which is facilitated by the eccrine gland activities of the palmar surfaces of the hands or plantar surfaces of the feet. The physiological parameters mentioned here are evidence of the workings of the body's various systems.

The sensory input of the biofeedback system comes in by way of the person's sensory receptors. Not only does the receptor receive the information, it also transduces it into electrochemical impulses. These are transmitted along neural pathways of the nervous system to the areas of the brain that are responsible for processing them.

CENTRAL MECHANISMS OF BIOFEEDBACK AND SOMATICS

What are the central mechanisms of biofeedback? With humans as our target animals, we cannot say for sure what the central mechanisms are. We can only piece together information from various sources. Biofeedback and somatics are learning experiences, so we can say that neural circuits are being activated by the learning experience. If we use Donald Hebb's theory of learning, we see that there is a functional process that eventually, through practice, becomes a structural change. The structural change involves the hippocampus in some way. There would be new synapses or facilitated synapses. Some circuits would be inhibitory, allowing for the release of a behavior. (Some neural circuits have the function of inhibiting movements or muscle contractions. When we inhibit the inhibiting circuits, this allows movement to occur.) Some would be activating, such as deeper stimulation affecting things like the basal ganglia.

In some cases, biofeedback activates unused circuits; in other, suppressed circuits are activated.

BIOFEEDBACK AND THE NERVOUS SYSTEM

What happens within the body/mind combination? Biofeedback is a prime example of the mind/body interface. The mind and body are inexorably intertwined; change one and you change the other. So let's take a look at the physiology with which the mind is interacting.

The central nervous system is made of up of the brain and spinal cord. The brain is the central processing unit for the rest of the physiology. It is made up of an estimated 100 billion neurons (this estimate changes over time, i.e., twelve billion used to be the standard estimate). The neurons can be classified as afferent (incoming information), efferent (outgoing information to muscles glands, or other parts of the brain) and internuncial (neurons that connect other neurons).

There are three systems that we now consider to transport information: the neural, the humoral, and the immune system. Neuronal pathways conduct information from the brain to the organs, glands, and muscles to promote appropriate functions and behavior. The humoral system of endocrine glands, which secrete directly into the blood of the circulatory system, serves to organize and activate behavior. The immune system, which has been considered a separate system from the intertwined neural and humoral systems, is now being seen as interconnected and subject to influences of neural/humoral fluctuations. For example, there is often a lowering of immune system function during bereavement.

Biofeedback is particularly concerned with neuronal activity, but it is indirectly affected by the humoral and even the endocrine systems. The transmission of neural information is easier to see, measure, and sense within the neuronal system. For example, if you neuronally send impulses to contract your forearm muscle, you can see immediate results. You can very quickly begin to make changes in the pattern of muscle contraction. You are quite used to doing that.

If we look at the cortex, we can see areas involved in biofeedback. Let's look at those areas. The cortex is an outer layer or layers of cells—neurons. It is made up largely of cell bodies with the remainder of the neuron extending subcortically. The axons of neurons extend down into the brain to synapse on other neuronal areas. There are about six layers of cortex, and the cortex is about ¼ inch thick. The surface area is about one square yard if flattened out, but it is folded and bunched to cover the rest of the brain and fit within the cranial cavity. The cortex is made up of folds and crevices. A fold is called a gyrus or gyri (plural), and a crevice is called a sulcus or sulci (plural).

Brain researchers have mapped out the functional areas of the cortex into what are called lobes. The cortical lobes include the frontal, parietal, occipital, and temporal lobes (Figure A.1). These lobes are not clear structural divisions of the brain, but they are somewhat anatomically and physiologically discrete. On the cortical surfaces there are primary sensory areas, secondary sensory areas, association areas, etc. The main function of the cortex is inhibition. It inhibits functions of the brain—movement, sensations—which originate at lower levels of the brain. Others are allowed to flow unimpeded. This enables us to engage in skilled movements. Spontaneous and exuberant, a child's behavior is an example of the cortex being unable to inhibit hosts of random movements. As the child gets older he becomes more and more able to engage in intentional movements and to conduct them with specificity and effectiveness.

Another area of interest is the parietal, occipital and temporal (POT) area, which is located in the region that includes the angular gyrus and the supramarginal gyrus. The POT area is the area where information comes together from a variety of sensory contributions; it helps give us a sense of a whole world.

From a left side view (left sagittal) of the brain, you can see the supramarginal gyrus and angular gyrus that have been considered part of the POT area. On the left hemisphere is part of Wernicke's area, which is involved with

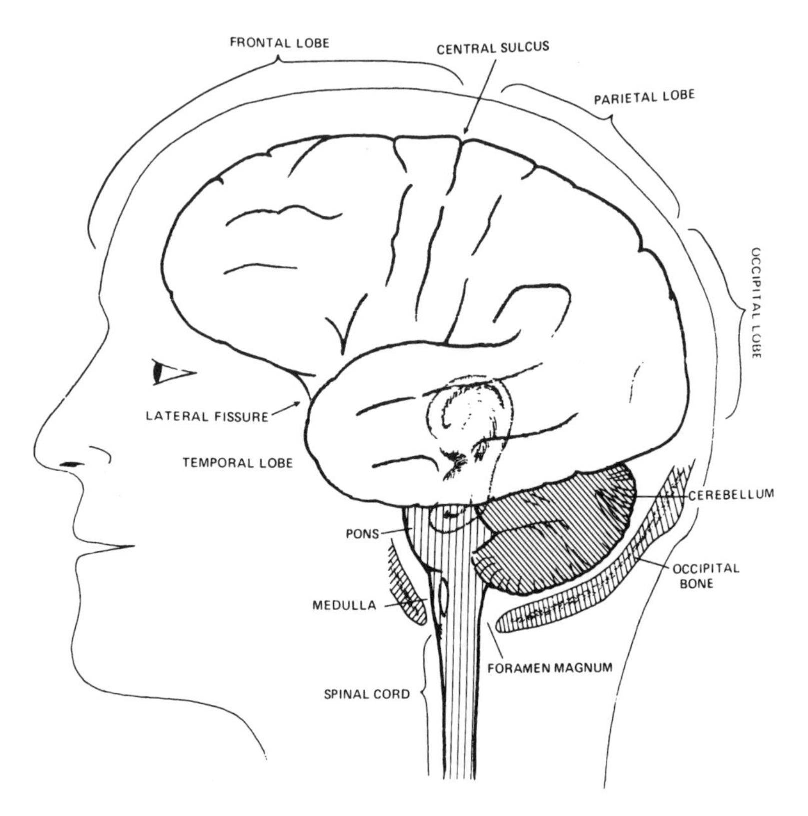

FIGURE A.1
The lobes of the cerebra cortex.

receptive, verbal processing. Farther forward is Broca's area which is involved with expressive verbal processing. Strokes in these two areas can result in expressive aphasia (damage to Broca's area) or difficulty speaking and receptive aphasia (damage to Wernicke's area) or difficulty with hearing or reading verbal material. Wernicke's area gives meaning to verbal production of Broca's area.

If we look at the outside of the cortex, we see that different areas are devoted to processing different sensory functions (Figures A.2A and A.2B). The superior (upper) surface of the temporal lobe is the primary auditory (hearing) area. The posterior (back) surface of the brain is the occipital lobe, which is devoted to primary visual processing. Devoted to sense of self, thinking,

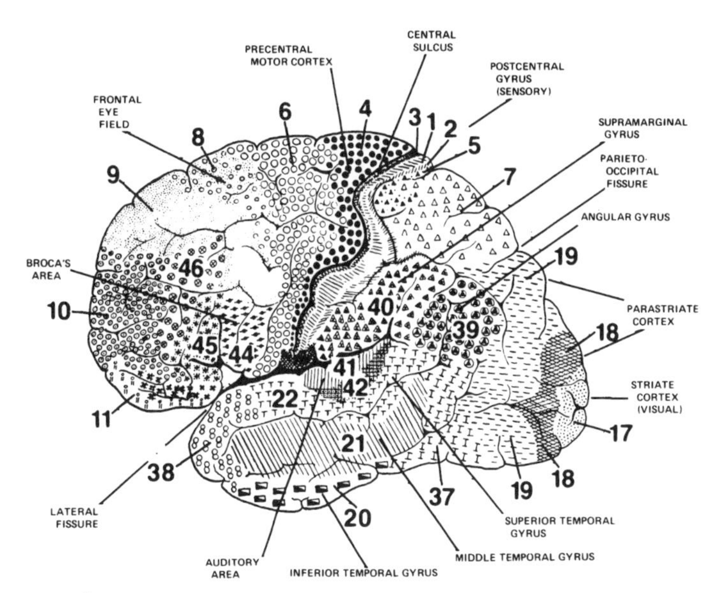

FIGURE A.2A

The major areas of the lateral surface of the cerebral cortex (after Brodmann).

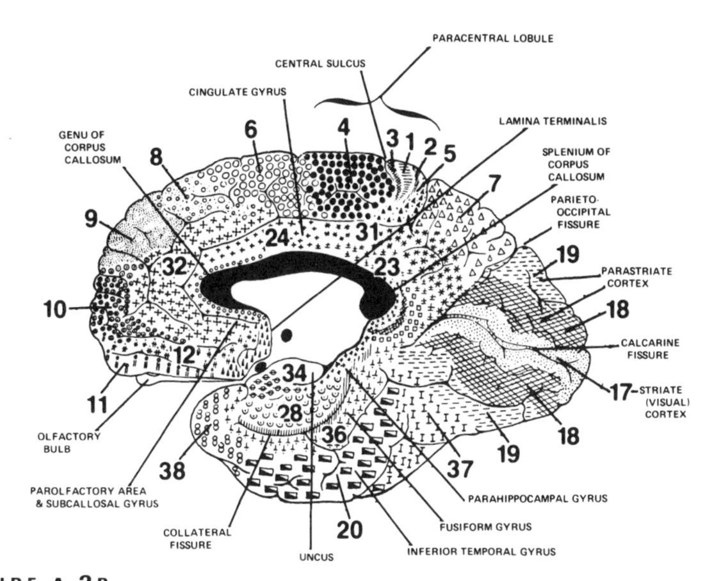

FIGURE A.2B

Same as above for the medial serface (after Brodmann)

anticipating future events, etc., the frontal lobe is the newest evolutionary unfolding. The precentral gyrus is the motor cortex. Mapped upside-down on the motor cortex with areas corresponding to the amount of control needed for movement is the motor homunculus. The post-central gyrus is devoted to the sensory cortex. Here you are mapped upside-down with areas corresponding to the sensory receptive areas of the body. The parietal lobe is right behind the sensory cortex and it is devoted to other body sensations, taste, etc. Other areas are devoted to receptive language processing or expressive language. Still other areas are association areas. Information from the primary and secondary sensory areas comes together to yield meaning via the association areas.

The corpus callosum is also involved in biofeedback. The corpus callosum is a fibrous bridge from one hemisphere of the brain to the other. It is made up of axons, the extensions from the cell bodies of the neurons. This fibrous bridge is thicker for women than men, indicating a greater bilateral organization for brain functions.

The superior colliculi, located in the midbrain, respond to change in visual stimulation; the inferior colliculi respond to the changes in auditory stimulation. Therefore, these two primitive sensory areas are involved or alerted by the biofeedback process.

Located deep within the brain is a series of structures called the limbic system. The limbic system includes the thalamus, hippocampus, amygdala, septal area, hypothalamus, etc. The structures form a circuit and are involved in emotions, motivations and memories. Each structure impacts on the next structure. Activity in the limbic system continues to spread from structure to structure throughout the system. Stimulation from the limbic system radiates out to the cortex and back again. In biofeedback training, the client learns how to tune down the activity of the limbic system. Self-regulation of the limbic system yields balanced emotional expression.

Sagittal View of the Brain A left sagittal view of the brain shows the following areas: the frontal, parietal and occipital cortex as it curves over toward the corpus callosum; the corpus callosum, the bundle of axons of cells whose cell bodies are located on one side and the remainders of which extend to the opposite hemisphere to synapse on neurons there; the pineal body (our primitive third eye, long thought to be a vestigial structure until J. Axelrod discovered the hormonal production of the pineal body, its response to changes in light which occur seasonally, and its production of melatonin); and the superior and inferior colliculi involved in visual and auditory reflexes respectively (Figure A.3).

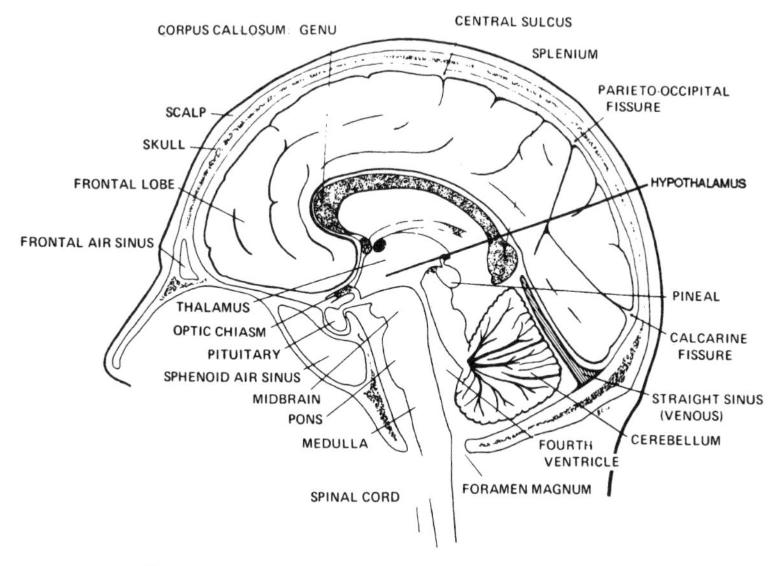

FIGURE A.3
A midsagittal view of the brain.

From the sagittal view you can see the thalamus, which is the switching station for the incoming sensory input having to do with the biofeedback signal—visual or auditory, lateral geniculate or medial geniculate body.

You can see the hypothalamus, which receives information from the alterations in sympathetic outflow signaled by the other physiological changes from the biofeedback process. The pituitary, of course, is involved in the process as the hypothalamus is tuned down in its impact on the pituitary in terms of hormonal output along the pituitary-thalamus-adrenal axis.

The medulla, located in the brain stem, is also affected by the general change in arousal fostered by the biofeedback experience.

The cerebellum will also be getting input as the other areas change in level of functions. The cerebellum contributes to sensorimotor coordination. When looked at functionally, it can be divided into three sections: the archicerebellum, paleocerebellum, and neocerebellum.

The sensorimotor cortex can be seen folding over toward the corpus callosum, which at this point is given information about the lower body and feet.

Subcortical Areas and Biofeedback Subcortical areas of the brain that are particularly affected by biofeedback include the hypothalamus, which is involved with emotions, motivations, and the origin of the sympathetic and parasympathetic nervous systems. The reticular activating system (RAS) is the fibrous (axonal) pathway coming from the body to the brain and from the brain to the body—it receives the stimulation input. It transmits it up to the thalamus, which conducts it out to the areas that need to be alerted to the new stimulation input. The RAS is located in the anterior portion of the brain stem. The medulla, another area that is involved in biofeedback, is the origin and endpoint for a number of the cranial nerves. It is located in the brain stem just beneath the pons. The medulla is the center for vital functions. Located here are the pacemaker cells for the respiratory system, blood pressure, heart rate, etc.

Basal Ganglia The basal ganglia are concerned with motor functions. They include the following structures: the globus pallidus (paleostriatum), which is the oldest structure; the caudate nucleus; and the putamen (neostriatum). The basal ganglia are part of the extrapyramidal motor system.

Thalamus The thalamus is a cluster of nuclei (a nucleus is a cluster of cell bodies of neurons located in the CNS). The thalamic nuclei are the locations of afferent sensory neurons (incoming to the brain) which synapse there before going on to the area of the brain that is responsible for processing the information. The thalamus also serves as a synapsing area of input coming up from the reticular activating system and other parts of the body on its way to parts of the brain.

The thalamus does not originate activity but serves as a switching station, redirecting the flow of activity or information. It relays somatosensory information to and from the primary sensory areas of the cortex.

Key thalamic nuclei for biofeedback include the medial geniculate nucleus (auditory) and the lateral geniculate nucleus (vision).

Limbic System The limbic system is located in the diencephalon. (The areas of the brain are referred to as the forebrain, the midbrain and the hindbrain. This is further divided into the telencephalon and diencephalon of the forebrain, the mesencephalon of the midbrain, and the metencephalon and myelencephalon of the hindbrain. The brain stem includes all the structures from the spinal cord to the midbrain, and sometimes is considered to include

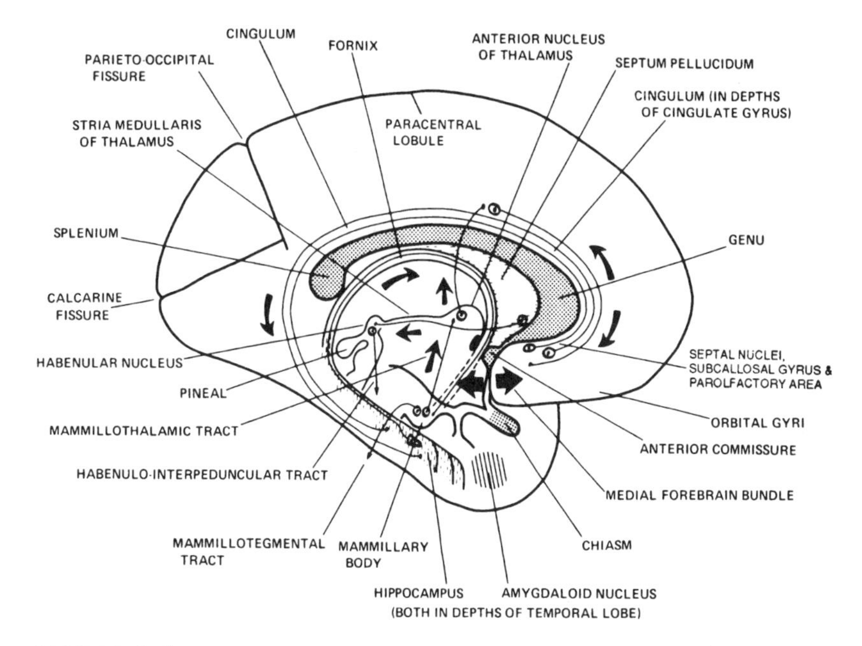

FIGURE A.4
The limbic system.

everything up to the cortex. Everything beneath the cortex is considered subcortical.)

The structures "in the limbic system include the hippocampus, amygdaloid nuclear complex, anterior part of the cingulate gyrus, uncus (rostral part of the parahippocampal gyrus), mammillary bodies, portions of the anterior hypothalamus and adjacent parolfactory area together with the subcallosal gyrus, the anterior nuclear mass of the thalamus, septum pellucidum, and habenular nuclear complex" (Garoutte, 1987, p. 188).

There are bundles of axons which connect the structures of the limbic system. The axonal bundles include the fornix, mammilo-tegmental tract, cingulum, diagonal band (of Broca), stria terminalis, stria medullaris of the thalamus, parts of the anterior commissure, and the medial forebrain bundle.

The limbic system is considered part of the old mammalian brain (Figure A.4). It is made up of a series of interrelated structures. The structures include the hippocampus, the septal area, the amygdala, etc. It is very involved in emotions. It has been referred to as the Papez circuit. The structures, once activated by the cortex, can continue to reverberate with output to the cortex and back repeatedly during emotionally charged experiences or reminiscences.

The olfactory bulbs bring olfactory information into this area of the brain, which has been referred to as the rhinencephalon, an ancient part of the brain. This area is particularly prominent and important for animals that depend on olfactory processing of the world to perceive and control behavior.

Some of the areas of the limbic system seem to be involved in experiencing pleasure. The so-called pleasure centers of the brain have been considered to serve as reward centers when we are pleased by our behavior or experience. These areas, when stimulated, yield pleasurable, diffuse sensations. This has been done with other animals and some humans. In biofeedback you can experience changes in limbic system activity.

Hypothalamus The hypothalamus is involved in biofeedback (Figure A.5). The hypothalamus, which is part of the limbic system, is involved with motivation, emotion, etc. The anterior (forward part) is part of the parasympathetic nervous system; the posterior is part of the SNS. For example, during warm weather the anterior hypothalamus is activated and we are forced into PNS dominance. Biofeedback facilitates shifts in autonomic nervous system dominance, and therefore, the hypothalamus.

The hypothalamus is a very important area of the brain with regard to biofeedback training. The hypothalamus has functions which include motivation, emotion and homeostasis. The motivations that originate there have to do with stopping and starting eating, starting and stopping drinking of fluids, and the various regulatory activities which have to do with homeostasis, that very important balance of physiological conditions that is necessary for healthy functioning and life.

The hypothalamus is the origin of ergotrophic and trophotropic systems of the body. The ergotrophic system energizes you and gets you ready for action and the trophotropic system get you ready for maintenance and repair. This is a useful distinction in relation to the SNS and PNS because it includes more than the hypothalamus down to the peripheral nervous system. It also includes an upward emphasis involving the cortical level of the brain as well. The SNS originates in the posterior hypothalamus; the PNS originates in the anterior hypothalamus.

Various areas of the brain and systems are particularly involved in the biofeedback process. The hippocampus, which is located in the limbic system,

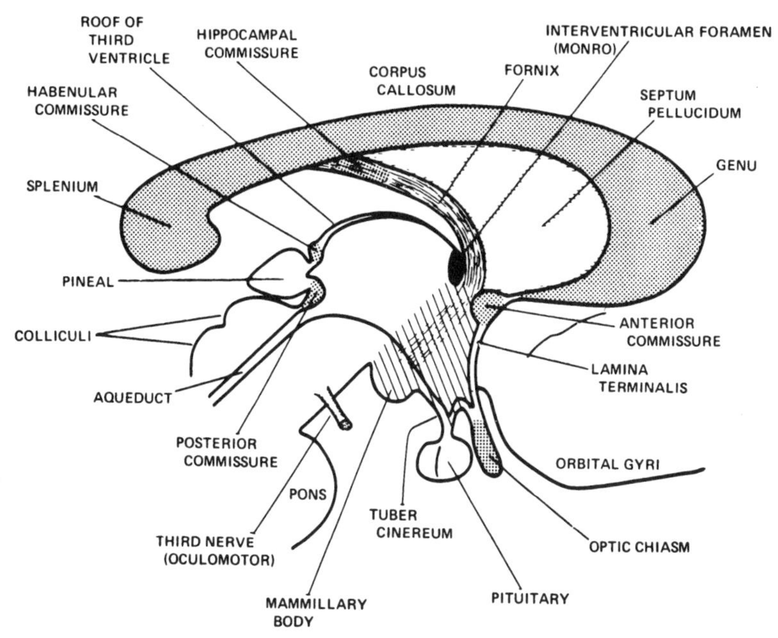

FIGURE A.5
Diagnonal hatch marks show the location of the hypothalamus.

is involved in putting information into long-term memory. With the learning involved in biofeedback, there is the concern that it will be permanent learning, i.e., that it will be stored in long-term memory.

Medulla The medulla is an area of the brain stem that is significantly impacted on by the biofeedback process. It is the area which is the origin of CN X, the vagus nerve. It is the location of the vital signs, the life support systems. Heart rate, blood pressure, respiration rate, etc., are all affected by the activity of the medulla.

With the psychophysiological changes fostered by biofeedback learning come alterations in activity of the medulla. As you learn to voluntarily control internal states you will be directly and indirectly affecting the function of the medulla. Ordinarily, the medulla receives its impulses to alter function by internal and external stimulation. It feels somewhat involuntary. But with the deliberate and unconscious alterations of biofeedback you begin to supply some of your own contributions to its activity.

Ventral View of the Brain From the ventral view of the brain (beneath, looking up), you can see the cranial nerves as they enter and leave their respective areas of the brain. The cranial nerves are sensory, motor, and mixed in function. They include CN I—the olfactory nerve; CN II—the optic nerve; CN III—the oculomotor nerve; CN IV—the trochlear nerve; CN V—the trigenimal nerve; CN VI—the abducens nerve; CN VII—the facial nerve; CN VIII—the auditory nerve (vestibulo-cochlear); CN IX—the glossopharyngeal nerve; CN X—the vagus nerve; CN XI—the spinal accessory nerve; and CN XII—the hypoglossal nerve.

The biofeedback experience brings information along CN II, III, IV, V, VI, and VIII. It affects outputs along CN II, X, and XI. Probably, all of the cranial nerves are involved to some degree in the biofeedback experience.

Neuron The neuron is a specialized cell, the basic information transmitting cell, in the nervous system. It is made of up a cell body, dendrites, axon and terminal buttons. The cell is contained by a cell membrane. The axon is wrapped in a protective sheath made up of glial cells called oligodendroglia within the CNS, and Schwann cells outside the CNS. The cell body has a nucleus, mitochondria (the energy producing organelles of the cell), microtubules, etc. Neurotransmitter or transmitter substance is produced in the cell body and transported to the terminal buttons in little packets called vesicles. These rupture into the gap between one neuron and the next to cross the gap called a synapse and the synaptic cleft and impact on the receptor sites on the dendrites, cell body or sometimes axon of the next cell. (They are like other cells in the body but they cannot replicate themselves or regenerate within the CNS).

The neuron outside the CNS has its cell body in the spinal cord or ganglia of the SNS, for example, but instead of synapsing on another neuron it synapses on another kind of cell such as muscle fibers or a gland.

An action potential is initiated by input to a neuron. If a neuron receives sufficient input from other neurons to cause a depolarization of the cell membrane, an action potential results. The neuron fires in an all-or-none process. An action potential is then conducted down the neuron without decline in strength due to the myelin sheath. The neuron synapses on another neuron or a muscle fiber. If it synapses on a muscle fiber, it causes a contraction of the muscle fibers.

In biofeedback the feedback signal is coming in along sensory pathways as a visual or auditory signal. It is processed by the primary sensory areas and then the secondary areas. It becomes translated into meaningful information which can be used by the brain to regulate the activity of the other areas. For example, μV information about EMG activity auditorily received can be used to lower somatic nervous system outflow to the muscles.

Nerve Pathways Information is conducted along the nervous system by way of neurons. The neurons are located within nerves, which are bundles of neurons covered by fascial sheaths. They also move along tracts, such as the medial forebrain bundle, which transmits information from one location within the brain to another. When they refer to fibers, they are referring to axons. Axons are the extensions of the neuron from the cell body to the terminal buttons. This extension may be short or quite long, such as within the motor system from the motor cortex to the location in the spinal cord from which the particular nerve exits, after a synapse, to go to the particular muscle or motor unit within the muscle.

At the inner surface of the cell membrane at the terminal button site, the vesicles cluster and then rupture into the synaptic cleft. After it has briefly affected the following neuron, the transmitter substance is neutralized or processed by re-uptake to remove it from the synaptic cleft so that the following neuron can return to its original state. It is as important to break the connection between neurons in the circuit as it is to make the circuit originally. If you did not break the circuit, you could not move on to the next event, neurologically.

Transmission of Neural Impulses When the information from the visual input, let's say graphed changes in biofeedback training, impacts on the retina cells, it is transduced by the retina cells into electrochemical impulses. These are conducted along neurons as action potentials. An action potential results from sufficient impact on the cell body or dendrites of a neuron. It comes in the form of neurotransmitter substance released by the previous neuron. It takes a number of neurons or repetition of input to bring a given neuron to its threshold of excitation. This decreases the electrical potential difference between the inside and the outside of the cell membrane to the point that there can be an opening of the cell membrane which allows a momentary reversal of the location of the chemicals. This wave of reversal and return to original position is very fast and spreads across the surface of the neuron until it reaches the myelin sheath. At each gap in the myelin sheath of a neuron there is a new action potential which recreates the original strength of the signal. This yields an event which "seems" to be jumping from one node of Ranvier to the next in a kind of jumping pattern called saltatory conduction. When this is graphed, it forms a wave form at the point that is being passed. This is called the action potential. When the action potential reaches the terminal buttons of the neuron, there is a secretion of neurotransmitter substance in the synaptic cleft which crosses the gap and affects the following neuron. The transmitter substance is created by the cell body of the neuron and conducted down the microtubules in little packets called vesicles.

Neurotransmitter Substance One of the significant features of neuronal activity is the secretion of neurotransmitter substance. Different neurons secrete different neurotransmitter substances. There were originally about six neurotransmitters delineated by brain researchers. Now there are fifty or more.

SENSATION

Sensory Input in Biofeedback Training Information about physiological changes comes to us via our sensory systems. It is possible to have a feedback signal come to us through any sense: vision, hearing, touch, smell, taste, balance. Biofeedback generally uses vision and hearing as its primary feedback channels. Tactile, smell, and perhaps taste feedback are probably happening at a subthreshold level. The biofeedback instrument provides visual input via meters, digital displays, lights, graphs and designs; the auditory input comes via sounds of varying pitches and patterns. The biofeedback trainer in the clinical setting also may provide visual and auditory input via vocalized encouragement or feedback of information, such as "You have now increased it a degree over last session." Facial expressions, body posture, and respiration patterns of the trainer may also form a human, social feedback source.

The other senses—smell, taste, touch—may feed back information from within the person. There may also be proprioceptive and kinesthetic feedback. As you are changing your body's degree of tension, there are accompanying psychophysiological changes. There may be changes in the olfactory input. These changes might come from your perception of the environment or your body. There are various subthreshold odors that you are responding to unconsciously. There may be tactile changes as your body changes its relationship to the tactile input from the chair you are sitting in or the clothes you are wearing or your body as it rests upon itself.

There may be gustatory changes on a subtle level as your body changes its biochemical balance, and therefore the taste in your mouth.

Proprioceptive, kinesthetic, vestibular changes may come to you from the change in your body's position or the feedback from your body as to what it is now doing as it moves toward relaxation.

A disproportionate amount of the brain is devoted to visual processing of your environment. Visual input to the brain comes in via cranial nerves. The advantage of visual input to biofeedback is that more specific information can be transmitted, i.e., quantities. The disadvantage is that you are drawn out of your inner sense when you attend to visual input.

Somethesia Somethesia refers to sensations from the skin (these are conducted by the cutaneous nerves), internal organs, and muscles. The sensations include touch or pressure, pain, warmth, and cold. The sensations are the result of input to different kinds of receptors. Biofeedback training deals with pain management, the experience of cold and the shift to warming the skin, and touch.

Biofeedback measures physiological signals that are too weak to be processed by our sensory receptors. Amplified or stepped up, the signals can then be perceived by our senses. Therefore, the biofeedback signal comes in primarily via the auditory (a sound signal) and/or visual (data, design display change, light change, etc.) signal. There are other areas of the brain that are stimulated by the biofeedback signal as it changes with our physiological fluctuations.

APPENDIX B

HOW TO DO YOUR OWN BIOFEEDBACK/SOMATICS TRAINING SESSION (ASSISTED OR SELF-GUIDED)

This is a sample program designed to enable you to conduct a biofeedback/ somatics session for others or yourself. It can be done with or without biofeedback equipment (computerized or stand-alone), with another guiding you or with you guiding yourself. In the future, it is possible that more and more biofeedback technology will be used at home because of the interactive multimedia systems that will be increasingly available. This means that people will be using programs and systems designed to be used on their home systems with menu-driven procedures for how to use the system.

SESSION I. ASSESSMENT

Look at yourself in the mirror or get a friend, practitioner, or relative to give you feedback about your posture. (This will give you a sense of where you are beginning.) You may want to take a stress test offered via computer or with paper and pencil.

Do you have any psychological or medical complaints? See an appropriate psychological or medical professional.

SESSION II. BASELINE RECORDINGS

Baseline recordings include physiological data derived from biofeedback recordings or a symptom or behavioral log. When working without biofeedback instrumentation, you can use your sense of your conscious and physical state. Subjective ratings can be used. (On a scale of 1 to 10, how would you rate your level of X? For example, pain, sense of well-being, or other.)

Determine your goals, short term and long term.

III. TRAINING SESSION

20 minutes: Talk to your trainer about the previous week, write in your journal, use a tape recorder or interactive computer program.
20 minutes: Practice biofeedback, relaxation practice, or somatics.
10 minutes: Conclude your practice and assess the results of your practice. Do a brief inventory. How are you feeling psychologically? How are you feeling physiologically? You might even want to use your subjective rating scale to evaluate on a scale of 1 to 10 how relaxed you feel. If pain is an issue for you, where is your pain level, from the least to the most pain you experience? Or you might assess your level of relaxation.

This is also a good time to visualize where you are going that day (short-term goals) or visualize your long-term goals.

IV. EVALUATION

If you have been using this protocol for work with a client or for initial training for yourself, you might pause or conclude the series after 10 weeks or so to evaluate your progress. How are you, relative to your original situation and your goals for yourself? You might move into a more informal ongoing practice in which you set aside 15 to 20 minutes per day (or even twice a day) to do a relaxation/somatics practice.

The book *The Relaxation and Stress Reduction Workbook* by Davis et al. has many useful scripts for relaxation practices. One somatic practice is the "Cat Stretch" Somatics Exercise series developed by Thomas Hanna. It is a series of movement patterns designed to remind your brain of the way it is managing its muscles. (It is not a traditional stretch routine.) It takes about 10 minutes to do after you've learned it. It makes a very useful daily maintenance series. It is presented in *Somatics* by Thomas Hanna. Audiotape and videotape versions of the Cat Stretch and other Somatic Exercises are available through Somatic Educational Resources, 1516 Grant Avenue, #212, Novato, CA; (415) 892–0617.

Cardiovascular workout two to three times per week, 20 minutes minimum, and daily somatic movements help your body remain flexible. Set aside 10 to 20 minutes per day to do a somatics practice. I would suggest the Cat Stretch. There are other somatics practices that would also be beneficial. The main goal is to do them slowly, gently, and with awareness. (It is not advisable to use traditional stretching as your somatics practice, because the muscle that is stretched triggers the stretch reflex. Sensory receptors in the muscle are sensitive to stretch and send messages to the spinal cord and back out to the muscle, causing it to recontract. It feels good at the time and the muscle does lengthen, but the stretch reflex causes it to recontract very quickly. If stretching is part of your repertoire, then at least follow it with some somatic movements that may counteract the negative effects of the stretch reflex.) Other somatics practices are also valuable.

APPENDIX C

STRESS MANAGEMENT PROTOCOL

This Stress Management Protocol has four steps: Assess your stress level, develop your plan, implement your plan, and evaluate your results.

I. ASSESS YOUR STRESS LEVEL

There are three areas of information for stress assessment:

1. Self-observable signs, i.e., stress symptoms you can observe (see self-observable signs of stress, p. 152).

2. Environmental assessment: Given the situation, would any reasonable human being be stressed? Then you probably are also, even though you might not be aware of it. (An extreme example might be following an earthquake; a milder example might be during final exams for students or even instructors.)

3. Internal environmental assessment: What are your cognitions or emotions at this time? Do you find yourself thinking about or telling other people how stressed or overloaded you are?

II. DEVELOP YOUR PLAN

1. Select your strategy. There are four basic strategies for managing your stress:

- Change your situation, if possible
- Leave the situation (temporarily or permanently)
- Remain in the situation and self-regulate your stress levels
- Change yourself after the event (or before, if possible)

2. Select your intervention(s)
    - Progressive relaxation
    - Autogenic training
    - Hypnosis (self-guided or guided by an audio tape)
    - Biofeedback
    - Visualization or guided imagery
    - Meditation
    - Cognitive restructuring
    - Benson's relaxation response
    - Stroebel's quieting response (see pages 138–139)
    - Your personal approach
    - Other

III. IMPLEMENT YOUR PLAN

IV. ASSESS THE RESULTS OF YOUR INTERVENTION(S)

If you have not achieved your desired stress reduction level, repeat the steps above until you achieve your desired level. (After practice using this protocol, you begin to be able to do it quite easily and quickly, if need be.)

APPENDIX D

BIOFEEDBACK AND SOMATICS RESOURCES

For information about certified biofeedback practitioners, professional training programs, Biofeedback Blueprint Knowledge Statements and biofeedback bibliography, and application packet for certification, contact the Biofeedback Certification Institute of America, 10200 West 44th Ave. #304, Wheat Ridge, CO 80033–2840, telephone (303) 420–2902. (They also have a *Biofeedback Study Materials Kit* available.) Your regional or state biofeedback society is also a good place to locate the certified biofeedback practitioners and training programs in your area.

For information on manufacturers and distributors of biofeedback equipment, and *Biofeedback Code of Ethics* and *Application Standards,* contact the Association for Applied Psychophysiology and Biofeedback, 10200 West 44th Ave. #304, Wheat Ridge, CO 90033–2840, telephone (303) 422–8436.

For information about somatics practitioners or professional training programs, contact the Somatics Society, 1516 Grant Ave. #212, Novato, CA 94945, telephone (415) 892–0617. They publish a newsletter with up-to-date listings. (Send a self-addressed, stamped envelope with your request.)

Somatics Magazine-Journal of the Mind/Body Arts and Sciences, 1516 Grant Ave. #212, Novato, CA 94945, is an excellent source of international developments (theory, practice, and research) in the field of somatics.

REFERENCES

Applications Standards Committee of the Association for Applied Psychophysiology and Biofeedback (1992). *Standards and guidelines for biofeedback applications in psychophysiological self-regulation.* Wheat Ridge, CO: Association for Applied Psychophysiology and Biofeedback.

Bandura, A. (1977) Self-efficacy: Toward a unifying theory of behavioral change. *Psychological Review, 84,* 191–215.

Basmajian, J. V. (1963a). Conscious control of single nerve cells. *New Scientist, 20,* 663–664.

Basmajian, J. V. (1963b). Control and training of individual motor units. *Science, 141,* 440–441.

Basmajian, J. V. (1974). *Muscles alive: Their functions revealed by electromyography.* (3rd ed.) Baltimore: Williams and Wilkins.

Basmajian, J. V. (1983). *Biofeedback: Principles and practice for clinicians.* (2nd ed.) New York: Williams and Wilkins.

Basmajian, J. V. (Ed.). (1989). *Biofeedback: Principles and practice for clinicians.* (3rd ed.) Baltimore: Williams and Wilkins.

Benson, H. (1975). *The relaxation response.* New York: William Morrow.

Berlyne, D. E. (1960) *Conflict, arousal, and curiosity* (p. 48). New York: McGraw-Hill Book Co.

Braud, L., Lupin, M., & Braud, W. (1975). *The use of EMG (electromyographic) biofeedback in the control of hyperactivity.* Paper presented at the Annual Meeting of the Association for Humanistic Psychology, Estes Park, CO.

Brooks, V. B. (1986). *The neural basis of motor control.* Oxford: Oxford University Press.

Brown, B. B. (1974). *New mind, new body: Biofeedback, new directions for the mind.* New York: Harper & Row.

Budzynski, T. H.(1969). *Feedback induced muscle relaxation and activation level.* Unpublished doctoral dissertation, University of Colorado, Boulder.

Budzynski, T. H., Stoyva, J. M., Adler, C. S., & Mullaney, D. J. (1973). EMG feedback and tension headache: A controlled outcome study. *Psychosomatic Medicine, 35,* 484–496.

Butt, D. C. (1987). *Psychology of sport: The behavior, motivation, personality, and performance of athletes.* (2nd ed.) New York: Van Nostrand Reinhold Co.

Christie, M. J. & Venables, P. H. (1972) Site, state, and subject characteristics of palmar skin potential levels. *Psychophysiology, 9*(6), 645–649.

Criswell, E. (1970). Experimental yoga psychology course for college students: A progress report. *Journal of Transpersonal Psychology, 1,* 71–78.

Criswell, E. (1989). *How yoga works.* Novato, CA: Freeperson Press.

Criswell, E. & Haight, M. (1976) The future of biofeedback in education. *Somatics, 1*(1), 22–26.

Davis, M., Eshelman, E. R., & McKay, M. (1988). *The relaxation and stress reduction workbook.* (3rd ed.) Oakland, CA: New Harbinger Publications, Inc.

Eaton, R. C. (1984). *Neural mechanisms of startle behavior* (p. 291). New York: Plenum.

Ezios, R. (1971). Implications of physiological feedback training. In J. Fadiman (Ed.), *The proper study of man* (pp. 465–476). New York: The Macmillan Company.

Feldenkrais, M. (1972). *Awareness through movement: Health exercises for personal growth.* New York: Harper & Row.

Fenz, W. D. & Epstein, S. (1967) Gradients of physiological arousal in parachutists as a function of an approaching jump. *Psychosomatic Medicine 29*(1), 33–51.

Friedman, M., & Rosenman, R. H. (1974). *Type A behavior and your heart.* New York: Fawcett Crest.

Fuller, G. (1977). *Biofeedback: Methods and procedures in clinical practice.* San Francisco: Biofeedback Press.

Fuller, G. (1980). *Behavioral medicine, stress management and biofeedback: A clinician's desk reference.* San Francisco: Biofeedback Press.

Gaarder, K. R., & Montgomery, P. S. (1977). *Clinical biofeedback: A procedural manual.* Baltimore: The William & Wilkins Co.

Garoutte, B. (1987) *Survey of functional neuroanatomy.* (2nd ed.). Mill Valley, CA: Mill Valley Medical Publications.

Gawain, S. (1978). *Creative visualization.* New York: Bantam Books.

Green, E., & Green, A. (1977) *Beyond biofeedback.* New York: Delacorte.

Green, E., Green, A., & Walters, I. (1971). *Biofeedback for mind/body self-regulation: Healing and creativity.* Paper presented at The Varieties of Healing Experience symposium, Cupertino, CA.

Haight, M. (1975). *Holistic education through imagery and biofeedback.* Paper presented at the Annual Meeting of the Association for Humanistic Psychology, Estes Park, CO.

Haight, M., Kamiya, J., & Jampolsky, G. (1974). *A biofeedback study in a high school.* Paper presented at the Sixth Annual Meeting of the Biofeedback Research Society, Monterey, CA.

Haines, R. W. (1932). The laws of muscle and tendon growth. *Journal of Anatomy, 66,* 575–585.

Haines, R. W. (1934). On muscles of full and of short action. *Journal of Anatomy,* 69, 20–24.

Hanna, T. (1980). *The body of life.* New York: Alfred A. Knopf.

Hanna, T. (1988). *Somatics.* Reading, MA: Addison-Wesley.

Hatch, J. P., Fisher, J. G., & Rugh, J. D. (1987). *Biofeedback studies in clinical efficacy.* New York: Plenum Press.

Helson, H. (1947). Adaptation-level as frame of reference for prediction of psychophysical data. *American Journal of Psychology, 60,* 1–29.

Helson, H. (1964). Adaptation-level theory: An experimental and systematic approach to behavior. New York: Harper & Row.

Hilgard, E. R., & Hilgard, J. R. (1975). *Hypnosis in the relief of pain.* Los Altos, CA: William Kaufman.

Holmes, T. H. & Rahe, R. H. (1967) The social readjustment rating scale. *Journal of Psychosomatic Research, 1,* 213–218.

Jacobson, E. (1938). *Progressive relaxation.* (2nd ed.) Chicago: University of Chicago Press.

Jung, C. G. (1917). *Analytical psychology.* New York: Moffat, Yard.

Kamiya, J. Operant control of the EEG alpha rhythm and some of its reported effects on consciousness. (1969). In C. T. Tart (Ed.), *Altered States of Consciousness* (pp. 507–517). New York: Wiley.

Kamiya, J., & Zeitlin, D. (1963). Learned EEG alpha wave control by humans. Report No. 183, Department of Mental Hygiene, Research Division, CA.

Karlins, M. & Andrews, L. (1972). *Biofeedback: Turning on the power of your mind.* Philadelphia: Lippincott.

Kimmel, et al. (1967). Instrumental conditioning of automatically mediated learning. *Psychological Bulletin, 67,* 337.

King, M. (1975). Biofeedback in the high school curriculum. *Association for Humanistic Psychology Newsletter.*

Luthe, W. (Ed.). (1969). *Autogenic therapy.* (Vols. 1–4.) New York: Grune and Stratton.

Maslow, A. H. (1971). *The farther reaches of human nature.* New York: Viking Press.

Mishra, R. S. (1973). *Yoga sutras: The textbook of yoga psychology.* Garden City, NY: Anchor Press/Doubleday.

Mulholland, T., & Gascon, G. A. (1973) Quantitative index of the orienting response in children. *Electroencephalography & Clinical Neurophysiology, 33,* 295–301.

Murphy, G. (1947) *Personality: A biosocial approach to origins.* New York: Harper.

Murphy, M. (1992). *The future of the body: Explorations into the further evolution of human nature.* Los Angeles: Jeremy P. Tarcher.

Nideffer, R. (1976). *The inner athlete: Mind plus muscle for winning.* New York: Thomas Y. Crowell.

Nideffer, R. M., & Sharpe, R. (1978). *A.C.T.: Attention control training.* New York: Wyder.

Nowlis, D. P, & Kamiya, J. (1970). The control of electroencephalographic alpha rhythms through auditory feedback and the associated mental activity. *Psychophysiology, 6*(4), 476–484.

Olton, D., & Noonberg, A. (1980). *Biofeedback: Clinical applications in behavioral Medicine.* Englewood Cliffs, NJ: Prentice-Hall.

Ornstein, R. (1972) *The psychology of consciousness.* New York: The Viking Press.

Paivo, A. (1971). *Imagery and verbal processes.* New York: Holt.

Paskewitz, D. (1983) Computers in biofeedback. In J. V. Basmajian (Ed.), *Biofeedback: Principles and practice for clinicians.* (2nd ed.) New York: Williams and Wilkins.

Pavlov, I. P. (1927). *Conditioned reflexes.* (F. V. Anrep, Trans.) New York: Dover.

Peffer, K. E. Equipment needs for the psychotherapist. In J. V. Basmajian (Ed.), *Biofeedback: Principles and practice for clinicians.* (2nd ed.) New York: Williams and Wilkins.

Peper, E., Ancoli, S., & Quinn, M. (Eds.). (1979) *Mind/body integration.* New York: Plenum.

Prokasy, W. F. & Raskin, D. C. (Eds.) (1973) *Electrodermal activity in psychological research.* New York: Academic Press.

Raskin, M., Johnson, G., & Rosdestved, T. J. W. (1973). Chronic anxiety treated by feedback-induced muscle relaxation. *Archives of General Psychiatry, 28,* 263–267.

Rickles, W., Sandweiss, J., Jacobs, D., Grove, R., & Criswell, E. (1983). *Biofeedback and family practice medicine.* New York: Plenum.

Rogers, C. R. (1951). *Client-centered therapy.* Boston: Houghton Mifflin.

Rogers, C. R. (1961). *On becoming a person.* Boston: Houghton Mifflin.

Rogers, C. R. (1980) *A way of being.* Boston: Houghton Mifflin.

Rotter, J. B. (1966) Generalized expectancies for internal vs. external control of reinforcement. *Psychological Monographs, 80* (whole number 609).

Samuels, M. & Samuels, N. (1975) *Seeing with the mind's eye.* New York: Random House.

Sargent, J. D., Walters, E. D., & Green, E. E. (1973). Psychosomatic self-regulation of migraine headaches. In L. Birk (Ed.), *Biofeedback: Behavioral medicine* (pp. 55–68). New York: Grune and Stratton.

Schultz, J. H. (1932). *Das Autogene Training. Konsentrotive Selbstents Pannung.* Stuttgart: Georg Thieme Verlag.

Schultz, J. H., & Luthe, W. (1969). *Autogenic training: A physiological approach in psychotherapy.* New York: Grune & Stratten.

Schwartz, G. E. (1975). Biofeedback, self-regulation, and the patterning of physiological processes. *American Science, 63,* 314–324.

Schwartz, M. (1987). *Biofeedback: A practitioner's guide.* New York: Guilford Press.

Seligman, M. E. P. (1973). Fall into helplessness. *Psychology Today, 71,* 43–48.

Selye, H. (1975). *The stress of life.* New York: McGraw-Hill.

Selye, H. (1974). *Stress without distress.* Philadelphia: Lippincott.

Sheer, D. (1975). Biofeedback training of 40 Hz EEG and behavior. In N. Burch & H. Altschuler (Eds.), *Behavior and brain electrical activity.* New York: Plenum Press.

Sperry, R. W. (1964). The great cerebral commissure. *Scientific American, 210,* 42–52.

Sperry, R. W. (1968). Hemisphere disconnection and unity in conscious awareness. *American Psychologist, 23,* 723–733.

Springer, S. P., & Deutch, G. (1993). *Left brain, right brain.* New York: W. H. Freeman and Co.

Steptoe, A. & Appels, A. (Eds.) (1989) *Stress, personal control, and health.* New York: Chichester.

Steptoe, A., Smulyan, H., & Gribbin, B. (1976) Pulse wave velocity and blood pressure change: Calibration & applications. *Psychophysiology 13,* 488–493.

Sterman, M. B. & Frier, L. (1972) Suppression of seizures in an epileptic following sensorimotor electroencephalographic feedback training. *Electroencephalography & Clinical Neurophysiology, 33,* 89–95.

Stern, R., & Ray, W. J. (1977). *Biofeedback.* Homewood, IL: Dow Jones-Irwin.

Stoyva, J. M. (1983) Guidelines in cultivating general relaxation: Biofeedback and autogenic training combined. In Basmajian, J. V. (Ed.) *Biofeedback: Principles and practice for clinicians.* (2nd ed.) New York: Williams and Wilkins.

Suinn, R. M. (Ed.). (1980). *Psychology in sports: Methods and applications.* Minneapolis, MN: Burgess.

Surwit, R. S. (1973). Biofeedback: A possible treatment for Raynaud's disease. *Seminars in Psychiatry, 5,* 483–490.

Turin, A. & Johnson, W. G. (1976) Biofeedback therapy for migraine headaches. *Archives of General Psychiatry, 33,* 517–519.

Vogel, W., Broverman, D., & Klaiber, E. (1968). EEG and mental abilities. *Electroencephalography and Clinical Neurophysiology, 24,* 1661–175.

Whatmore, G., & Kohli, D. R. (1974). *The psychophysiology and treatment of functional disorders.* New York: Grune and Stratton.

White, L., & Tursky, B. (1982). *Clinical biofeedback: Efficacy and mechanisms.* New York: Guilford Press.

Wickramasekera, I. (1976). *Biofeedback, behavior therapy, and hypnosis.* Chicago: Nelson-Hall.

Wolpe, J. (1958). *Psychotherapy by reciprocal inhibition.* Palo Alto, CA: Stanford University Press.

Wolpe, J. (1973). *The practice of behavioral therapy.* New York: Pergamon Press.

Wolpe, J. (1980). Behavior therapy for psychosomatic disorders. *Psychosomatics, 21,* 379–385.

Yates, A. (1980). *Biofeedback and the modification of behavior.* New York: Plenum.

Yerkes, R. M., & Dodson, J. D. (1908). The relation of strength of stimulus to rapidity of habit formation. *Journal of Comparative Neurological Psychology, 18,* 459–482.

INDEX

ABOUT THE AUTHOR

Eleanor Criswell-Hanna, Ed.D., is Professor of Psychology and former Department Chair of the Psychology Department, Sonoma State University, California. She has been involved with the field of biofeedback since 1967 and has taught biofeedback at Sonoma State University since 1969. The Professional Biofeedback Training sequence at Sonoma State University was developed in 1981. She has taught biofeedback classes in Mexico, Australia, and the United States. She is a past president and former executive director of the Biofeedback Society of California. In 1975 she co-founded, with Thomas Hanna, the Novato Institute for Somatic Research and Training. She trained in somatic education with Thomas Hanna in his 1981 Australian training program, and worked closely with him in the development of the field of somatics over the years. She is currently serving as president of the Somatics Society and editor of *Somatics.* A licensed psychologist, she maintains a private practice in psychotherapy, biofeedback, and somatic education. *How Yoga Works: An Introduction to Somatic Yoga* and *Biofeedback and Somatics* are two of her recent books.